THE PHENOMENA OF DEPRESSIONS

THE
PHENOMENA
OF
DEPRESSIONS

ROY R. GRINKER, SR. M.D. *Director, Institute for Psychosomatic and Psychiatric Research and Training, Michael Reese Hospital and Medical Center, Chicago*

JULIAN MILLER, M.D. *Adjunct Psychiatrist, Institute for Psychosomatic and Psychiatric Research and Training, Michael Reese Hospital and Medical Center, Chicago*

MELVIN SABSHIN, M.D. *Professor and Head, Department of Psychiatry, University of Illinois College of Medicine, Chicago*

ROBERT NUNN, M.D. *Clinical Assistant in Psychiatry, Institute for Psychosomatic and Psychiatric Research and Training, Michael Reese Hospital and Medical Center, Chicago*

JUM C. NUNNALLY, Ph.D. *Professor of Psychology, Vanderbilt University, Nashville, Tennessee*

Hoeber Medical Division

HARPER & ROW, PUBLISHERS
New York, Evanston, and London

PUBLISHED DECEMBER 1961

THE PHENOMENA OF DEPRESSIONS
Copyright © 1961 by Hoeber Medical Division
of Harper & Row, Publishers, Incorporated
Printed in the United States of America

Library of Congress Catalog Card Number: 61-14624

CONTENTS

Preface

THIS BOOK CONTAINS THE RESULTS OF A RESEARCH program on depressions from a phenomonological point of view. We do not consider this as an esoteric, introspective attempt by psychiatrists to extend their awareness of the boundaries between patients' normal and abnormal processes, but as an attempt to describe accurately the clinical processes of depressions and to evolve logical and useful classifications of subgroups or categories. From these categories we hope that correlations will be made with data from other disciplines, from genic, developmental, and follow-up studies, and from therapeutic results. Such correlations with a wide number of clinical, biological, and biochemical variables might then lead the research of psychiatrists, psychologists, and psychosomatists to fulfillment of our ultimate goal of a deeper, more complete understanding of the causes, natural history, and treatment of various types of depressions.

This is the first publication of the results of our investigations, which were begun in 1954 shortly after preliminary discussions of the general subject of depressions in 1953. For the reader we believe that the development of our methods of observations, data collecting, and data analysis is as important as our results. Therefore the research is presented in chronological order, beginning with a review of the literature and formulation of the research. The presentation of the pilot and full-scale studies includes discussions of the problems of poor psychiatric observations, the difficulties in ascertaining precipitating causes, premorbid personalities, and the psychodynamics of the phenomenon. The subgroups or categories of depressions derived from the studies and a general summary conclude the text.

In a program of investigation lasting over six years many personnel changes were bound to occur. Ultimately the "hard core" of interested and available persons consisted of only the present authors. But among those who began the study with us and who had to leave it for various reasons were Drs. David Hamburg, Francis Board, Arnold Tobin, and Robert Drye. During the early months Dr. Sam Beck gave us valuable advice concerning the Q-sort technique which he had used to great advantage in his studies on *The Six Schizophrenias* (1954).

We gratefully acknowledge the assistance of the following psychiatrists, who while serving as residents participated in the ratings of the full scale study: Drs. Peter Barglow, Arthur Kling, David Marcus, Paul Miller, David Roth, Marjorie Barnett, William Cohen, Arnold Goldberg, Marvin Herz, Ethel Isaac, Richard Telingator, Michael Basch, Daniel Schiff, Daniel Shapiro, and Ralph Wadeson. Furthermore, the following nurses gave us invaluable assistance in the ratings of current behavior on the hospital nursing units: Misses Waltrant Schoenberger, Margaret McCorkindale, Doris Ellinger, Elizabeth Wasson, Ruth Helmke, Louise Palacios, Ruth Reiss, Merle Pray, and Mrs. Miriam Kaplan.

R. R. G.
J. M.
M. S.
R. N.
J. C. N.

Chicago

Introduction

DEPRESSION AND MELANCHOLIA, THE LATTER A
term devised by the ancient Greek physicians, are synonymous,
although neither is well defined. As Lehmann (1959) points out,
the diagnosis of depression may refer to a symptom, a syndrome,
or a nosological entity. Despite its vagueness, depression is one of
the most frequent diagnoses made on admission and at discharge
for patients in psychiatric units of general hospitals and in private
mental hospitals.

FREQUENCY OF THE DIAGNOSIS OF DEPRESSION

It is difficult to compare the frequency of depressions among
inpatients and outpatients applying for care in State, Federal, and
nongovernmental hospitals. On one hand, the symptom of depression may mask a wide variety of psychiatric entities, and, on the
other hand, the syndrome of depression may be hidden by many
other presenting and leading symptoms. The kinds of patients admitted and the diagnostic criteria and skills utilized by the staffs

This investigation by the Institute for Psychosomatic and Psychiatric Re-
search and Training of the Michael Reese Hospital and Medical Center,
Chicago, was generously supported in its entirety by Grant 54-126 from the
Foundations Fund for Research in Psychiatry.

of the two types of institutions are usually quite different. The diagnosis of depression is thus a global and inaccurate label.

It may be of interest to scan the statistics published by the National Institute of Mental Health of the U.S. Department of Health, Education and Welfare on patients in mental institutions during 1957, the last available report. The statistics as stated in the report have many limitations, but they furnish an overview of frequencies of admissions according to diagnoses. For our purposes we can only use three items under the heading of psychotic disorders, since we cannot determine how many depressions are included under various types of neuroses, reaction types, and personality disorders.

In those public mental hospitals reporting, close to 15 per cent of psychotic patients are classified under the headings of involutional psychoses, manic depressive psychoses, and psychotic depressions. The ratio of females to males is almost two to one. In the private mental hospitals approximately 50 per cent of the psychotic first admissions belong to the same three nosological entities, and the ratio of females is also about two to one. It is obvious that the admission rate of depressions for psychiatric units of general hospitals and private mental institutions is over three times that of public mental hospitals without including the vast number of neurotic depressions and other conditions overlying a depressive core.

Perhaps this may be explained by the fact that governmental hospitals only receive late, more typically psychotic, and unsuccessfully treated patients or patients with a different type of depression. If the wage-earner of the household is able to work, he is more likely to seek private care rather than state hospital care at first for his female dependents. Even though he must pay at least part of the costs himself in association with his insurance benefits, he is told that most depressions are of short duration and treatable. The public mental hospitals usually receive the chronic intractable cases after modern therapies have failed.

When the patient's depression is considered severe enough, either because it is associated with self-destructive fantasies or previous suicidal attempts or threats, or if the patient is markedly agitated or sleepless and disturbs his family either at night because of these symptoms or during the daytime by his clinging complaining attitudes, the psychiatrist usually hospitalizes his patient immediately. He does this not only to protect the patient and the family, but also for the purpose of determining and implementing the suitable treatment.

It is a curious phenomenon that, although depressions are so frequent, not only in hospital practice but also among ambulatory patients seeking clinic and private office care, very few investigations have been made on this syndrome as contrasted with the intensive work carried out on schizophrenic, psychosomatic, and other psychiatric conditions. Psychiatric residents-in-training tend to become bored with the apparent stereotypy of complaints and symptoms. The psychiatrist often relies on the patient's description of symptoms for the diagnosis of depression; in fact, the patient very frequently begins the diagnostic session by complaining that he is depressed. His facial expression, inhibited thinking, retarded movements, agitation, and dry mouth often confirm his own diagnosis. Further direct questioning reveals with little effort on the part of the examiner that most of the usual psychosomatic concomitants of depression are also present.

INEXACT NATURE OF THE DIAGNOSIS

It seems as if the psychiatric profession has taken for granted that all that can be known about depressions has already been discovered and thoroughly described. As a matter of fact, one finds, as we shall show later in our survey of the literature, that clinically relatively little new has been added to the description of depressions in general since antiquity. Textbook descriptions of this entity are stereotyped accounts which have been copied from book to book and repeated from generation to generation. For example, the latest American textbook on psychiatry (Arieti, 1960) reproduces almost identically the descriptions found in Kraepelin's (1912) old textbook of psychiatry. This is all the more strange since the term *depression* is a description of a predominating affect and gives no clue to the underlying processes, the nature of the patient's problems, the predisposing factors, or the precipitating causes. As an affect which may dominate the mood of individual patients, depression may be a symptom of a wide variety of psychological problems and accompany almost any clinical nosological entity.

Furthermore, the mood of depression which leads one to make a diagnosis of this entity is not so easy to determine. It may be hidden and masked by a wide variety of behavioral or psychological defenses. Many patients cover up depressive feelings with smiling, gay, and joking exteriors. Others deny primary sadness but attribute worry to single symptoms such as insomnia, gastrointestinal distress, headaches, etc., or complain of boredom or fatigue. Still others present compulsive doubts or hypochondriacal preoccupations, dissociated states, or paranoid delusions.

The diversity and wide range of depressions may be exemplified by the fact that many depressed patients, who gravitate to a public mental hospital after repetitive electric shock treatments or failures in psychotherapy, make a good adjustment. But their depressions reappear when these patients are threatened with discharge from the hospital and a return to responsible existence in their ordinary social environment. These patients are extremely infantile and dependent, and they have collapsed initially after the real loss of a significant supporting figure. After going through periods of alcoholism, frequently homosexuality, and drug addiction, they find their haven in a mental hospital and lose the affective mood of depression, which only appears when their passive existence is threatened (Oken *et al.,* 1960). Contrast this with the commonly observed guilt-laden patient in the psychiatric unit of the general hospital who castigates himself vigorously and ceaselessly because he is not active, enterprising, and competent in supporting his family or in achieving success in his profession. Clinical observations like these strongly suggest the existence of more than a single type of depression.

Other examples of the wide range of psychiatric problems for which patients enter a psychiatric hospital with the diagnosis of depression are, on the one hand, the middle-aged woman, and, on the other, the young adult of either sex. The former react with varying degrees of boredom, sadness, and hopelessness to the current or approaching end to their roles as mothers, housekeepers, and significantly needed figures in the family, as at the same time their procreative functions have ceased. Contrast this with young adults with life's satisfactions before them but who become depressed at separation from a protected environment, or when confronted by minor stresses preliminary to a schizophrenic breakdown. Do depressive syndromes in young people, like the so-called "benign stupor" and intercurrent manic attacks, presage a schizophrenic process? How closely is the depressive affect an index of fatal diseases and of carcinoma in particular? How does one differentiate the paranoia associated with depressions from other paranoias?

At present we find very few examples of patients with mania or circular alternating mania and depression. The diagnosis of manic-depressive psychosis is rarely necessary in modern times. However, we do have a number of nosological entities in our current nomenclature, requiring us to make such discriminatory diagnoses as psychotic depression, manic-depressive reaction, involutional psychotic reaction, transient situational personality disturbance, and personality disorders, all of which usually are associated with depression, and the ability of the psychiatrist to differentiate them is challenged. Thus, we are confronted with the question that has never been answered as to whether depression is a disease, a psychiatric entity, a psychological reaction type, or a symptom of one or several underlying psychological problems.

The lack of knowledge concerning the natural history of psychiatric entities was pointed up for the schizophrenias at the introduction of insulin shock therapy when there were no available statistics for spontaneous remissions to compare with the results of the new treatment. Depressions in the preshock and predrug era were treated by support, opiates, and often institutionalization. The middle-aged and elderly patients were presumed to become fixed and intractable, especially when cerebral arteriosclerosis supervened. But how long depressions lasted, what kinds of cases recovered quickly or not at all, the frequency and duration of remissions, and a host of other questions were not adequately answered.

In recent years more practical questions have arisen, a few of which may be cited. How do depressions superimposed on premorbid hypochondriasis and obsessional states differ from others, since both of these are frequently unresponsive to electric shock treatment? Has the premorbid personality a significance in relation to the precipitating causes and the characteristics and course of the syndrome? What is the actual relationship of involution to depression? What is the relation of depressive affect to the onset and course of psychosomatic or, for that matter, of all somatic diseases? What types of depression, if any, do the modern antidepressive drugs benefit?

These and many other questions cannot be answered until the vast diagnostic category of depressions is broken down into meaningful entities which can be correlated with a host of variables.

CLINICAL OBSERVATION IN PLACE OF PSYCHODYNAMIC STEREOTYPES

After the depressed patient has been admitted to the hospital and the symptoms and behavior have been carefully noted, the psychiatrist or resident usually formulates the problem in psycho-dynamic terms. These formulations are usually highly stereotyped and vary little from patient to patient. It is usually stated that the orally fixated patient has had some narcissistic blow or is suffer-ing from the loss of narcissistic supplies, which provokes rage against an object lost in reality but whose image is retained in-ternally. By and large, however, this originally imaginative hypoth-esis has led to the development of stereotypes of depression, and alternative hypotheses have not been carefully explored.

An unfortunate by-product of focusing on the dynamics of depression has been the underemphasis on sound clinical observa-tions and adequate descriptions of these and other mental pa-tients. As a matter of fact, most of American psychiatry is dynamic psychiatry, and the word *descriptive* has become an appellation of derogation. Descriptive psychiatry is considered to be old-fashioned and obsolete. Clinical psychiatry is incompletely taught in most of our training centers because the teachers themselves are less interested in it, since they for the most part have been trained to infer and formulate rather than to describe. As a result, the details of clinical syndromes are little known, and the natural history of psychiatric diseases has been neglected.

Furthermore, clinical somatic correlations with basic psycho-physiological processes in depression have been lacking with the exception of a few recent investigations. If there are any consti-tutional, physiological, and biochemical bases for the psychotic depressions which reappear regularly, often without known pre-cipitating factors, and which have a high familial incidence, their details will not be uncovered by our current techniques.

We became interested in the phenomena of depressions since people with this syndrome are so frequently admitted to psychiatric hospitals. Are there different types of depression which can be recognized clinically? Do these types correlate with different etiologies, predispositions, and precipitations? Are there different clinical categories of depression that can be determined by adequate observations and detailed recordings of their clinical states, spontaneous progress, and responses to therapy?

We believe that our planned empirical approach to depression, which simply means observations of behavior, feelings, and concerns and an adequate description of course and response to therapy, can also support a growing urge to revive sound clinical psychiatry in this country. In so doing we do not negate the impetus that psychodynamics had made in understanding people with psychiatric difficulties, but we believe that a great deal has been lost by abandoning careful clinical observations and denigrating the descriptive techniques.

CHAPTER 1

An Overview of the Literature on Depression

SINCE EARLIEST RECORDED TIMES THE SYNDROME OF depression has plagued mankind and occupied the attention of layman and physician alike. In fact, no more accurate description of a clinical depression can be found than in the Old Testament's Book of Job. It is obvious that we can only sample the tremendous literature from various periods: ancient, German descriptive and nosological, twentieth-century psychoanalytic, modern American and English reports, and empirical-behavioral studies.

THE ANCIENT LITERATURE

We are especially indebted to J. R. Whitwell (1936) and Gregory Zilboorg (1941) for their painstaking investigations into the ancient roots of our concepts regarding *all* mental illness. Comparisons between modern and ancient ideas are somewhat difficult because similar terms often have different meanings. The ancients classified mental illness into the large categories of epilepsy, mania, melancholia, and paranoia. However, by mania was meant all those mental illnesses characterized by abnormal excitement, and melancholia described all patients with abnormal depression whether associated with physical or psychological

1

disturbances. Furthermore, clinical descriptions of mental disease emphasized physiological etiology in that various humors were supposedly significant in the development and symptomatology; hence, the name melancholia, which literally means "black bile."

A sudden flux of bile to the brain was believed to bring on unpleasant dreams and anxiety and a superabundance of black bile caused melancholia. However, as Drabken (1950) tells us, Caelius Aurelianus disputed the notion that black bile was the cause of melancholia; it was only vomited through the esophagus. Aurelianus considered that melancholia was more frequent in middle age and, contrary to our current findings, that it rarely occurred in women. He studied the antecedent causes and believed them to be indigestion, the use of drugs, grief, fear, and other circumstances. The signs of approaching melancholia were mental anguish and distress, dejection, silence, animosity toward members of the household, a longing for death, suspicion on the part of the patient that a plot was being hatched against him, weeping without reason, meaningless muttering, distension, and other physical symptoms.

It is interesting that quotations culled by Whitwell from the ancients who concerned themselves with mental disturbances all include in their classifications the term *melancholia,* meaning many things, but many of them closely related to our current notion of depression. Thus, Aretaeus discussed melancholia and mania as alternate phases of the same disorder, quite similar to the manic-depressive concept developed later by Kraepelin. He wrote about a young man afflicted by melancholia who was cured by falling in love with a girl. "The physician could not cure him, but love did." He also wrote about cure through occupational therapy in the case of a joiner who recovered by concentrating on tasks in his workshop.

Zilboorg, in his investigations of the ancient writings, found that Plutarch (46-120 A.D.) left a description of a depressed person which is still meaningful to twentieth-century psychiatrists:

When a man is depressed, every little evil is magnified by the frightening spectres of his anxiety. He looks on himself as a man whom the gods hate and pursue with their anger. A far worse lot is before him. He dares not employ any means of averting or remedying the evil lest he be found fighting against the gods. The physician, the consoling friend, are driven away. "Leave me," says the wretched man, "me the impious, the accursed, hated of the gods, to suffer my punishment." He sits out of doors wrapped in sackcloth or in filthy rags. Ever anon he rolls himself naked in the dirt, confessing about this and that sin. He has written, eaten, or drunk something wrong. He has gone some way or other which the Divine Being did not approve of. The festivals in honor of the gods give no pleasure to him but fill him rather with fear. He proves in his own case that the saying of Pythagoras is false that we are happiest when we approach the gods, for it is just then that he is most wretched. Temples and altars are places of refuge for the persecuted, but where all others find deliverance from their fears, there this wretched man must most fear and tremble. Asleep or awake, he is haunted alike by the spectre of his anxiety. Awake he makes no use of his reason, and asleep he enjoys no respite from his alarms. His reason always slumbers; his fears are always awake. Nowhere can he find an escape from his imaginary terrors.

This is, of course, a description of the most frequent type of depression—that associated with agitation, accurate to the point of amazement. Furthermore, the idea that as a man approaches the gods, becoming successful, he is likely to develop a depression, is quite similar to our frequent formulation that a depressed person is often cracked on the rock of success, and kindliness makes him worse because of his guilty feelings. Likewise, one is struck by the contrast of Plutarch's description to the allegorical description of Job's depression in which guilt was vigorously denied.

It is not necessary to belabor any further the point that the ancient physicians were able to distinguish a series of symptoms that comprised the syndrome of melancholia, a name which designated their primitive etiological thinking. Nevertheless, their observations were accurate. We still hold to the idea that depression and maniacal excitement are related as two sides of the same coin.

They knew something about the predisposing personality types, and they were aware of some of the precipitating factors. The ancients also knew that depression was a self-limited, although chronic, illness and adequately described the so-called recoveries or long remissions.

GERMAN DESCRIPTIVE AND NOSOLOGICAL LITERATURE

As Zilboorg points out, the nineteenth century was an era of system-building characterized by classifications of mental illness. Kraepelin was the leader of a new era in psychiatry, which emerged gradually and methodically from the work of many people after the "First Psychiatric Revolution" in the sixteenth century, when humanistic scientific-medical approaches replaced demoniacal ideas of etiology. However, the most distinguishing feature of Kraepelin's contribution was his attempt to establish the natural history of the various entities that were included in his classification.

Not only were etiology and diagnosis emphasized, but prognosis was based on the study of the end stage of various illnesses. Kraepelin tried to demonstrate that mental illness, like other diseases, ran a regular course. He attempted to unite psychiatry with medicine in his emphasis on hormonal, metabolic, and physiological etiology. No matter how much criticism can be directed toward the artificiality of the Kraepelinian system or depreciation of it as purely descriptive, the fact is that the Kraepelinian classification for a long time seemed satisfactory, enduring as it did until after World War II.

Furthermore, some of his descriptions of various psychiatric entities hold to this day and have not been improved upon, as evidenced by the fact that much of current American literature is simply a copy of Kraepelin's writings. Certainly the neglect of the individual in the Kraepelinian classification was satisfactory until recently for the psychiatrists who worked in governmental mental hospitals. For the most part these were poorly trained and over-worked physicians who spent more energy in staff conferences determining what diagnosis fitted the patient's symptoms than in learning about him as an individual.

Kraepelin described depression as developing gradually, pre-ceded for months and even years by indefinite prodromal symp-toms. The patients first become sad, dejected, and apprehensive, finding no enjoyment in their work or families. They are over-shadowed by doubts, fears, and self-accusations. They complain of feeling dull, confused, and forgetful. Among the symptoms are delusions of guilt; they become retrospective and refer to many misdeeds in their past life; often insignificant facts are recalled and blown up to great proportions. They sometimes feel that they have been guilty of actual destructive acts toward members of their families and find themselves wicked in the eyes of God, who has forsaken them.

Kraepelin made much of the hypochondriacal delusions in de-pression, which indicates that he confused the depression of hypo-chondriasis and the depression occurring without such preceding chronic symptoms. He also included depressions with hallucina-tions of hearing when patients referred to a punishing inner voice that commanded them to commit suicide. At one time he also described involutional melancholia as a separate entity, which is still maintained in our current official classification.

Another observation made by Kraepelin was the almost invari-able anxiety accompanying depressions, now described when present as an agitated depression. Also in Kraepelin's description was the lack of interest in the environment and the dull, sluggish, and indifferent attitude which the depressed patient expressed. Forgetfulness and apathy often remained after the depression lifted. Here probably he was referring to the depressions which accompany the presenile dementias.

When depressed, the patient sees only the dark side of life. The past and the future are alike, full of unhappiness and misfortune.

Life has lost its charm. The patients become unsuited to their environments, are failures in their work, lose religious faith, and live from day to day in gloomy submission to their fate. They take no pleasure in life and do not care to live longer. They are ill-humored, gloomy, shy, pettish, or anxious, and sometimes irritable and sullen.

In another context Kraepelin wrote about compulsive symptoms, indicating again that the premorbid personality of many depressed patients expresses itself in exaggerated form during the illness. He also wrote about the retarded and withdrawn depression in patients who sit helplessly before their meals, unable to feed or care for themselves.

It is clear that Kraepelin observed and described practically all the symptoms that are known today as characteristic of the stereotyped and most frequently encountered depressions. He also combined symptoms characteristic of groups of patients and of their premorbid personalities into separate entities with the idea that these represented types of depressions. Thus he wrote about the involutional depression, the depression associated with mania in alternation or in mixed form, the depression with hypochondriasis, the depression with compulsivity, the depression with hallucinations and delusions, and finally the most frequent depression associated with simple retardation.

Bleuler (1911) in his textbook discussed depression at considerable length. He described depression as being a flat and colorless affective state in which patients complain that they have no emotions. The expression is painful, desperate, anxious, usually with very little mobility, but the rigidity of affects as in schizophrenia is not present. The patient is unable to shed tears even though he may distort his face in sobbing.

Bleuler stated that the association of ideas is retarded even to the point of disturbance of sensory perceptions. All thoughts are difficult and create an internal psychic pain. Bleuler discussed the delusions of economic, bodily, and spiritual ruin. These take many forms, depending upon the individual personality, but all of them indicate the patient feels that he has sinned in a dreadful manner and nothing can save him. He has committed crimes, and even the slightest mistakes are delusionally blown up to mean something terrible. He is to blame for everything that has happened in his personal life and in the world at large. His behavior corresponds to his feelings.

Again Bleuler, like Kraepelin, emphasized that anxiety may predominate in the form of restless movements, clinging to people, excessive wailing, and sleeplessness. He pointed out that nearly all melancholics have suicidal impulses, some form of depersonalization, and compulsive ideas. When hallucinations, which may be paranoid or delirious, appear, Bleuler termed the condition melancholic insanity. All depressives have three cardinal symptoms: depressed mood, mental retardation, and inhibition of the will.

The majority of patients become ill with their first attacks between fifteen and thirty years of age, and the melancholic episodes seem to increase in frequency with age. Many patients have attacks which resemble one another so closely that an exact photographic repetition has been described. Bleuler wrote that, if one knows the history of previous attacks and the healthy intervals between, the diagnosis is easily made. If there have been no previous attacks, then the diagnosis can only be made by the elimination of other diseases since there are no specific signs or symptoms of manic-depressive insanity. Indeed, mania or depression appearing in early life may be the first sign of a future schizophrenic breakdown.

The later German psychiatrists whose work was summarized by Lange (1928) placed a great deal of attention on the premorbid personality of persons susceptible to the manic-depressive psychoses. Prior to the overt outbreak of a psychosis, episodes of milder attacks are usually experienced. The Germans emphasized the importance of heredity and its expression in particular constitutional defects. The depressive person was supposed to have a pyknic body build, the short, stocky bodily configuration. The emotional aspects of this constitutional factor were considered to be a fundamentally inherent sad temperament and cyclic swings of mood. Among the symptoms that seem to precede depressions are a hypochondriacal attitude toward the self and a compulsive sensitive attitude toward others.

In summary, the technique of observation and description of the clinical manifestations of depression and the classification of the syndrome into subtypes reached its height from the efforts of German psychiatrists before World War I. Between the two World Wars, a great deal of work was done on heredity and constitutional factors in the etiology of melancholia. Beginning in the early 1930's, the clinical descriptive method fell to low esteem and has not been revived. Instead, the German descriptions have been copied over and over, and modern psychiatrists, more influenced by psychoanalytic theory, focus on the internal psychodynamics of individual patients.

TWENTIETH-CENTURY PSYCHOANALYTIC LITERATURE

"The Second Psychiatric Revolution" occurred in the twentieth century with the advent of Freud and psychoanalytic theory, knowledge, and technique which underemphasized nosology and group prognosis but concentrated on individual psychodynamics. This represented a great advance in the understanding of mental illness, but, as we shall mention later, its fascination almost to the exclusion of every other approach has involved considerable loss.

Freud (1917) reported his first systematic observations on depressions in his classical paper, entitled "Mourning and Melancholia." In this he distinguished between the ordinary reactions of grief depression. He recognized that even in descriptive psychiatry the definition of melancholia was uncertain and that the various clinical forms did not seem to warrant reduction to unity. His observations were made on a small number of cases, the psychogenic nature of which he felt to be indisputable. He described the distinguishing mental features of melancholia as: "a profoundly painful dejection, abrogation of interest in the outside world, loss of the capacity to love, inhibition of all activity, and the lowering of the self-regarding feelings to a degree that finds utterance in self-reproaches and self-revilings and culminates in a delusional expectation of punishment."

He was struck with the similarity to many traits seen in grief, with the exception that in grief the fall in self-esteem is absent. "In grief the world becomes poor and empty; in melancholia it is the ego itself."

The key to the clinical picture was in Freud's perceiving that the self-reproaches are really against a loved object whose image has shifted onto the patient's own ego. His reconstruction of the process is that:

An object-choice, an attachment of the libido to a particular person, had at one time existed; then, owing to a real slight or disappointment coming from this loved person, the object-relationship was shattered. The result was not the normal one of a withdrawal of the libido from this object and a displacement of it on to a new one, but something different, for whose coming-about various conditions seem to be necessary. The object-cathexis proved to have little power of resistance and was brought to an end. But the free libido was not displaced on to another object; it was withdrawn into the ego. There, however, it was not employed in any unspecified way, but served to establish an identification of the ego with the abandoned object. Thus the shadow of the object fell upon the ego, and the latter could henceforth be judged by a special agency, as though it were an object, the forsaken object. In this way an object-loss was transformed into an ego-loss and the conflict between the ego and the loved person into a cleavage between the critical activity of the ego and the ego as altered by identification.

From this reconstruction he inferred that on the one hand there must have been a "strong fixation to the loved object" and "on the other hand, in contradiction to this, the object cathexis can have had little power of resistance. This seems to imply that the object choice had been affected on a narcissistic basis, so that, when obstacles arise in the way of the object cathexis, it can regress into narcissism." He thus included among the special characteristics of melancholia, a "regression from object cathexis to the still narcissistic oral phase of the libido."

It is the sadistic side of the ambivalence directed toward the lost object, which has now become one with the ego, that explains the self-abuse, self-punishment, and the self-destructive tendencies:

Just as mourning impels the ego to give up the object by declaring the object to be dead and offering the ego the inducement of continuing to live, so does each single struggle of ambivalence loosen the fixation of the libido to the object by disparaging it, denigrating it and even as if it were killing it. It is possible for the process in the *Ucs.* to come to an end, either after the fury has spent itself or after the object has been abandoned as valueless.

Abraham (1953) became interested in depressions in 1911 and at first was under the impression that "depression is to grief as anxiety is to fear." In 1924 he advanced the idea that in melancholia there is a regression to a primitive oral level (cannibalistic) as evidenced by the introjection and incorporation of the lost love-object. Abraham recognized the dynamic similarity between obsessional neuroses and depressions, both being characterized by a high order of ambivalence, not only in the acute phases, but also in the quiescent periods. Thus they both are related psychologically to the same pregenital phases. However, in regressions the obsessional neurotic retains his love-object, the melancholic regresses to the oral-sadistic phase and loses his love-object.

Abraham then suggested a number of etiologic factors which he felt were involved in the precipitation of the illness. These included a possible constitutional factor, a special fixation of the libido on the oral level, a severe injury to infantile narcissism brought about by successive disappointments in love, and finally, the occurrence of the first important disappointment in love before the Oedipus wishes have been overcome. The last etiologic factor suggested is the repetition of the primary disappointment in later life, and this is seen to be the exciting cause of the onset of melancholic depression. He also suggested the occurrence in childhood of a primal depression setting the pattern for the recurrence in later life.

Melanie Klein (1948) contends that the mechanisms of projection and introjection, operative at or near birth, are connected with developmental stages which she terms the "paranoid" and the "depressive" position. She postulates an infant in constant conflict between libidinal and aggressive drives, basing this in part on Freud's duality of life and death instincts. The "paranoid" position precedes the "depressive" and results from a fear of destruction of the ego from internal persecutors. These fears may in turn be reprojected. As the child attains a point of maturation when he can recognize the existence of a single object toward whom are directed both love and hate and who can be loving (giving) and hating (frustrating), he fears for destruction (loss) of the object, and since his differentiation between self and object is incomplete, he fears for the destruction (loss) of his internal "good" objects. Part of this fear of loss Klein believes comes from his own destructive and greedy fantasies. Thus, for her, the basic "depressive" fear is of loss of the internal objects with consequent disintegration of the infant's inner world. It is the reactivation of this infantile depressive position which is related in adult life both to mourning and to melancholia. The failure to establish firmly the good internal object predisposes the individual to an exaggerated reaction (depression) to losses in later life. She assumes that the attempt to incorporate the lost object is accompanied by an attempt to reinstate the original internal objects (parents) which have also been lost in response to the "realistic" loss. She believes that there is only a quantitative difference between "normal" mourning and depression.

Elizabeth Zetzel (1953) attempts to explain the concept of depression and to review the structure of mental development that Klein has formulated. She states that there are three assumptions involved: first, the existence of innate sexual knowledge (with the result that the Oedipal conflict exists early in life); second, the dominant role ascribed to the death instinct; and third, the importance attributed to the processes of introjection and projection. Klein feels that her theory must be accepted or rejected in total, and here Zetzel disagrees; one can discuss her ideas about ambivalence and the early defense mechanisms without accepting other aspects of the theoretical structure. Her feeling is that the most important contribution of Klein is her conception of the growth of object relationships in an early ambivalent setting. She feels that neither the theoretical framework or reconstruction of specific fantasies rest on sound evidence.

Edith Jacobson (1953) considers depressions as belonging to the manic-depressive group, and hence as basically a psychotic illness. This is a critical differentiation for her since she believes that "psychosis" in contradistinction to "psychoneurosis" represents not only a mental but an unknown psychosomatic process. She thus asserts that a somatic component tacitly accepted but little discussed by most authors is an essential and differentiating component of depressive illness, acknowledging at the same time the difficulty in making the diagnostic differentiation. She feels that "true cyclothymics will experience their slowing up quite dfferently from the way depressive neurotics experience their inhibition."

She describes a complicated and highly theoretical metapsychology of the depressive process, in which she tries to outline her conception of the shifting identifications related to depression, recognizing that Freud's original formulation did not adequately discuss the intrapsychic changes that accompany the internalization of the ego–object conflict, as a lost object is introjected.

Jacobson regards an insufficient separation between object and self-representations as characteristic of these patients. The lack of distinct boundaries between them accounts for the patient's too strong fixation to parental love-objects. The patient gauges love-objects and self by infantile value measures, predominantly by their omnipotent power and invulnerability. "The fear of a 'loss of the object' is fear of a destructive absorption of the 'good, powerful' object-image by the self-image." Either success or failure may arouse an "initial hostile derogation of the love object, which cannot be tolerated." This leads to a reflux of aggression from object-image to self-image, leading to a devaluation of both. This she believes to be the primary depressive disturbance, while manifestations such as clinging, masochistic submission, sadistic provocation, retreat from the object world, and introjection of the conflict represent secondary attempts at restitution or defense.

On the other hand, Therese Benedek (1956), in discussing the universal nature of a depressive constellation, develops the origin of this state in the psychobiology of the female procreative process itself. The term *depressive constellation* "designates a core organization of opposing, instinctual tendencies and their primary object representations." Benedek feels that each phase of procreative growth brings about a regression to the oral phase of development, showing, on the one hand, receptive-retentive tendencies and, on the other hand, active-giving attitudes. Birth is a traumatic separation for both mother and child and the relationship is reestablished on an alimentary, oral level: "Through the repetition of hunger and satiation, the biologic unity is replaced by psychological communications through introjections and projections."

"Through memory traces of alimentary experiences, the infant introjects the 'good-feeding mother equals good-satiated self.' " Images of good mother promote confidence and hope in the child, at the same time that the mother develops confidence in her own motherliness, projecting this gratification back upon the child. Failures in gratification result in crying fits, and in total regression to the undifferentiated phase in which mother as object did not exist. As he calms, the aggressive impulses are introjected, establishing the equation "bad mother equals bad self." Thus this ambivalent core of personality is formed which subsequently may predispose to depression whenever anything initiates regression to the oral level.

Edward Bibring (1953) criticizes the trend in the psychoanalytic literature to concentrate on a single type of depression, although he finds superficial acknowledgment of the existence or possibility of other types. He sees depression as "the emotional expression of a state of helplessness and powerlessness of the ego; irrespective of what may have caused the breakdown of the mechanisms which established self-esteem." He thus sees more than one predisposing constellation and feels that the "orally-oriented" type so commonly referred to is only the most common. He views depression as resulting from the tension in the ego between its narcissistic aspirations and its perception or its (real or imaginary) helplessness and incapacity to live up to these aims. According to this view depression is not primarily determined by a conflict between ego and id or superego, but stems from a tension in the ego itself, an intrasystemic conflict. "Depression is the emotional correlate of a partial or complete collapse of the self-esteem of the ego. . . ." It is thus a basic ego-state similar to anxiety, elation, or well-being. Bibring is almost alone in not ascribing depression specifically to the vicissitudes of aggression.

On essentially these themes there have been many variations, accretions, and subtractions by such authorities as Rado (1928), Edoardo Weiss (1944), Fenichel (1945), Mabel Cohen *et al.* (1954), Gero (1936), etc. One should also include Spitz' (1945) description of hospitalism as a syndrome in infants which bears many resemblances to a depressive state. In subsequent work Spitz (1946) termed this *anaclitic depression.* Finally, Herbert Rosenfeld (1959) wrote an extensive review article on the subject of depression. He defines points which constantly come up for discussion, very few of which have elicited real controversy and disagreement although, regarding the so-called depressive position and the early superego, there is considerable variance between the school of Klein and that of others in England as well as most of the American psychoanalysts. There are, however, many differences of opinion about phases of early infantile development which are antecedent or predisposing to the depressions that develop in later life.

One is struck by the preoccupation not only of the early analysts but their successors as well with theory. Rarely does an author demonstrate the source of his theoretical conclusion. Most papers on depression contain discussions which are purely theoretical and concerned with the demonstration of forces, energy distribution, libidinal concentrations, and means by which attitudes and affects can be transformed from one function or structure of the mind to another. Clinical data when supplied are useful in discussing the symptomatology and the meaning of the precipitating factors, but too often there is an immediate jump into a theoretical discussion of what has happened among the allocated portions of the mental apparatus without appeal to evidence.

Mendelson (1960), while this book was in preparation, reviewed the psychoanalytic concepts of depression which considerably amplifies what we have abstracted. He states that the psychoanalytic literature is less a manifestation of a "great investigation" than of a "great debate." To Mendelson the literature seems to be a "not-so-great-monologue."

From these theoretical psychoanalytic discussions there has developed a stereotype of the psychodynamics of depression which is unrelated to the variations in the clinical picture. It is this stereotype which has influenced psychiatrists today to assume that, once given the symptomatology of depression, the formulation of the psychodynamics can be reeled off with facile fluency. These basic formulations, stereotyped though they may be and agreed upon as they are by so many, have never been validated and, despite their universal acceptance by many authors, they are far from applicable to individual cases or groups of cases.

MODERN AMERICAN AND ENGLISH REPORTS

The American literature on depressions is summarized in three great volumes: the Association for Research in Nervous and Mental Disease report on "Manic Depressive Psychosis," Volume II published in 1931; the volume on *Depression* edited by Hoch and Zubin in 1954; and the chapter on "Manic Depressive Psychoses" in the *American Handbook of Psychiatry,* published in 1959, edited by Arieti.

Elliott states in the *American Handbook:* "As variable as its clinical picture, as unconfirmed as its dynamic interpretation remains today, as controversial as its etiology continues to be, manic-depressive psychosis nevertheless strikes the student of psychiatry for its relative simplicity and for the facility with which its nosologic concept is grasped even by the beginner." This statement made as late as 1959 reveals the characteristic impact of depressions on the psychiatrist when viewed from the standpoint of the presenting mood. The differences and variations in the modes of expression and the concomitant effects on thinking and behavior are minimized, thus artificially making depressions a stereotyped and unitary concept.

Arieti (1959) uses the term *psychosis* to indicate that the psychopathological way of living is accepted by the patient and becomes his way of relating to people and of interpreting the world. Unfortunately this excludes that wide variety and great number of individuals who complain bitterly in their depressions that they are "not themselves" and ignores those depressed patients who actively, vigorously, and with a great deal of anxiety fight their disorders as if they were imposed upon them from the outside. He divides the symptomatology of depression into three areas: (1) a pervading feeling of melancholia; (2) a disorder of thought processes characterized by retardation and unusual content; and (3) psychomotor retardation and, in addition, accessory somatic dysfunctions.

In reviewing the American literature one finds a striking indecision about the precipitating factors and how these relate to the development of the psychosis. Despite the fact that these authors lean heavily on an hereditary–constitutional etiological theory, when they try to link the precipitating factor to the depression they quote extensively from the psychoanalytic literature. So, for example, Henderson, Gillespie, and Batcheler (1956) write about a constitutional factor in the form of inherited accentuation of all erotism, a fixation of libido at the oral level, and a severe injury to infantile narcissism which is repeated as a disappointment in later life, and is the exciting cause of the depression.

Three grades of severity are mentioned: simple or mild; acute; and depressive stupor, which is a repetitious account of the German descriptions. However, there is little evidence by which to differentiate patients in the three categories. In the depressive stupor there seems to be more withdrawal. In the acute depression there seems to be a more severe reaction than in the simple depression and not as much withdrawal as in the stuporous type. However, there is no sharp differentiation among these states, and they seem only to indicate depth or severity rather than any essential etiology or prognosis.

Again in the involutional type, Henderson, Gillespie, and Batcheler describe depression without retardation, anxiety, feeling of unreality, and hypochondriasis, etc. There is no one symptom peculiar to the involutional period, but because it occurs at a certain time in life the name of this period implies an hypothesized important etiological factor. The premorbid compulsive character, as most clinicians have observed, is particularly emphasized. The idea of impending death or uselessness stimulates a loss of interest in life and the development of a conflict in which at one and the same time there is revulsion from death and a wish for it.

Norman Cameron (Arieti, 1959), in his discussion of functional psychoses, points out that Kraepelin in his successive editions of his textbook wrote a clinical history of modern psychiatry. At one time he differentiated six varieties of depression: simple, stuporous, severe, paranoid, delusional, and delirious. In addition, he postulated mixed states which he called: depressed mania, agitated depression, depression with flight of ideas, and depression with partial inhibition. In his eighth and final edition Kraepelin put all of these forms into one syndrome called manic-depressive insanity, with the exception of the involutional depression, which he still maintained was due to disturbances of metabolism, nutrition, or endocrine function. However, there is still a notion that reactive depression, due to external disappointments, is different from the endogenous depression which is considered to be constitutional and, in severe cases, psychotic. Cameron himself distinguishes three groups of depressions: the retarded depression, the anxious depression, and the involutional depression.

Muncie (1948) describes depression as a reaction in which the dominant fixed mood of sadness or its equivalent appears. This results in a general slowing and reduction of activity, loss of initiative, and ideas of unworthiness and self-depreciation. Depression of a pathological type is a major reaction of greater depth and fixity than the so-called normal depressions.

Among the physiological alterations are insomnia, poor appetite, weight loss, reduction in sexual functions, general reduction in tone of musculature, and periods of slow motility. There is atonic constipation, low blood pressure and pulse rate. Muncie also describes depressions with anxiety, sometimes reaching the point of panic. Here there are marked disturbances of sleep, restlessness, tremors, accelerated pulse, heightened blood pressure, and sometimes elevated temperature. In hypochondriacal depressions the presenting complaints are those of concern with health associated with fatigue, headache, and other various sensations in the body which move from place to place and are characteristically worse in the morning.

We would be remiss if we neglected to mention Lewis' (1936)

extensive summary of the literature on depression. He adds nothing to the clinical description of depression that has not already been cited, but he does indicate the disappointing demonstration that short cuts and clear signposts for diagnosis do not exist in this disorder and that prognostic signs are deceptive. He also comes to the conclusion that depressions constitute a wide range of disturbances with a variability of end results. Thus, it is extremely difficult to classify patients in order of favorable results or of duration of attack. He states that manic-depressive psychoses constitute a provisional group of heterogeneous disorders. It is often disconcerting that we have to confess that we cannot find a clear and easy way to answer our questions about the future in such an illness.

In this country an extensive review of manic-depressive psychosis was made by Bellak (1952), who considers the disease not as an entity but as a syndrome caused by many etiological factors. He speaks of "multiple factor psychosomatic theory of manic-depressive psychosis." He believes that the classification includes a certain number of shared phenomena and consists of several widely differing syndromes with different etiological factors which may range all the way from anatomic to biochemical, endocrine, genetic, infectious, neurophysiological, and psychological.

EMPIRICAL-BEHAVIORAL STUDIES

Since we began our researches into the phenomena of depressions in 1954 several excellent papers have appeared which indicate that other workers have also become interested in observing, describing, and re-evaluating the syndrome. For example, Roth (1959, 1960) has written two comprehensive reviews of depressions from several viewpoints: clinical, EEG, course, and responsiveness to treatment. Lichtenberg (1957) brought a fresh point of view to the subject by classifying depressions according to ego functions evidenced in orientation to tasks and to expectancies of success or failure in generalized goals, personality styles, and particular situations. Engel and Reichsman (1956) in their studies of an infant with a gastric fistula correlated analysis of gastric contents, mood, and behavior in response to the presence or absence of a known person.

Lehmann (1959) in a review article points out that, in contrast to anxiety, "virtually no experimental animal data on depressive states are available because no experimental model exists at present for depressive states in animals." He does cite in animals, however, naturally occurring states which look like reactive depressions following the loss of master or mate. There is a similar dearth of research data on experimental depressions in humans, again because of the difficulty in producing this phenomenon in the laboratory.

In defining the depressive syndrome Lehmann states there are both primary and secondary symptoms.

A group of *secondary symptoms* comprises: feelings of hopelessness; hypochondriacal preoccupation; feelings of depersonalization; obsessive-compulsive behavior; ideas of self-accusation and self-depreciation; nihilistic delusions; paranoid delusions; hallucinations; suicidal ruminations and tendencies. Insomnia, anorexia, and weight loss are usually associated with depressive states, and various autonomic, metabolic, and endocrine abnormalities might be present.

"The secondary symptoms of depression are less regularly found than the primary, and among the *primary symptoms,* the sad, despairing emotional state and the depressive mood seem to constitute the real core of all depressions in which the psychiatrist is interested." He states that the differentiation between so-called normal and pathological depressions manifested by mourning and melancholia is often only one of degree. He believes that the distinction between endogenous and reactive depressions is a valid one but admits that often it is difficult to make.

Lehmann believes that such terms as psychotic, alcoholic,

senile, and schizophrenic depression are descriptive only. He suggests seven approaches to the field: "phenomenological," etiological, somatotype descriptions, accurate delineations of the premorbid personality, the natural history of the disease, the autonomic disturbances, and the neuropharmacological responses.

Cleghorn and Curtis (1959) outline the number of physical symptoms masking depressions, such as aching muscles, paresthesias, hypochondriasis, autonomic disturbances, gastrointestinal disturbances, impotency, amenorrhea, vasomotor disturbances, sleep alterations, feeding disturbances, and weight loss. Huston (1956) also lists a wide variety of physical symptoms which mask depressions and lead to mistaken diagnoses.

Cassidy *et al.* (1957) report on a quantitative study on 100 manic-depressive patients compared with 50 medically sick controls. In comparing symptoms between medically ill and manic-depressive patients they found that such medical symptoms as headache, blurred vision, dyspnea, palpitation, anorexia, weight loss, nausea, abdominal pain, constipation, urinary frequency, dysmenorrhea, pains, and weakness among others occur in high frequency in manic-depressive disease. In the psychological sphere, symptoms such as poor concentration, slow thinking, low mood, anxiety attacks, the feeling of having a poor memory, fear of losing one's mind, suicidal thoughts, and expression of low expectancy of recovery from illness seem to be much more characteristic of manic-depressive disease.

Viewing depressions from the opposite point of view, Schmale (1958) has studied the relation of depression to the onset of somatic disease of all types. Loss of a love-object leads to feelings of helplessness or hopelessness. However, this loss or separation may not only be real, but also threatened, expected, or fantasied loss of an object of gratification—real or symbolic, internal or external, conscious or unconscious. Depression results from an inability to replace the real or phantasied loss. The actual, threatened, or symbolic loss is thought to be antecedent to the precipitation of a wide variety of diseases. However, Board (1957) found that adrenocortical and thyroid hormonal levels were elevated in depressives who were withdrawn, retarded, and dry and who were unable to express their feelings adequately, indicating that hopelessness and helplessness are not always accompanied by depression of biological or essential functions.

Recently a descriptive study on depressions has been published by Hamilton (1960), who has developed a rating scale that he considered useful in quantifying the results of an interview with 49 exclusively male patients. His rating of 17 values includes global traits rather than specific traits. This encouraged the raters to connect traits according to what they thought belonged together. Thus his study only elicited a small number of factors. These four factors include: (1) retarded depression without gastrointestinal symptoms; (2) depression with many somatic symptoms, disturbed sleep, and agitation without anxiety; and (3) depression with anxiety-reaction. These factors do not portray the classical syndromes of depressions; yet the author attempts to correlate his factors with such diagnoses as endogenous and reactive depression and with the results of treatment.

In summary, there has appeared in the American literature on depression a recent trend toward more accurate clinical description, tests of biological functions, a longitudinal view of the course of the illness, and an experimental-observational study of the human infant. Each of the few papers quoted has discussed depression from a single objective frame of reference. The paucity of this work and the scanty results hardly warrant as yet a synthesis into a new composite picture. Nevertheless the current trends are healthy. They do not theorize as to what the infant thinks or feels by reconstructive anthropomorphizing; nor do they simply recapitulate the early clinical descriptions. Rather, a new approach has developed which revives sound observations, descriptions, and experiments using a wide range of methods, which may ultimately lead to a conceptual synthesis of a psychosomatic process.

SUMMARY

An overview of the literature on depressions reveals that the clinical observations and descriptions begun by the ancient physicians have not been essentially improved through the ages. In the nineteenth century, scientific-medical developments overthrew the demonological approach to the etiology of mental disorders. Systems of classifications culminated in the work of Kraepelin, whose categories of depressions persist even today. The twentieth-century Freudian influence emphasized psychodynamics to the exclusion of clinical psychiatry and Kraepelinian clinical descriptive stereotypes were replaced by stereotyped psychodynamic formulations. Lately an empiric-behavioral approach has been revived, not in isolation, but in association with physiological, endocrinological, and pharmacological methods. However, clinical correlations with the relatively accurate variables measured by these methods require the breakdown of the global syndrome of depression into discrete, empirically derived, subcategories.

~~~~~~~~~~~~~~~~~~~~~~~~~~

CHAPTER 2

The Formulation
of the Research

In 1953, THE SENIOR AUTHOR INVITED SEVERAL individuals to meet monthly with him for informal discussions about the problems of depressions. Included in the group were Drs. Therese Benedek, James E. P. Toman, Thomas Szasz, Fred Robbins, and Richard Renneker. This combination of psychiatrists, psychoanalysts, and a physiologist engaged in a lively and stimulating discussion of theoretical concepts, but nothing particularly new developed. It became apparent that mutual edification must eventually be superceded by concrete research operations devised to to obtain reliable data on what depressed patients felt and how they behaved.

THE PREPARATION

For this purpose a four-man research group was formed composed of senior and junior psychiatrists and analysts who, after working out a tentative research design, invited the participation of six senior residents. Because of graduation from residency, departure from the city, loss of interest in the project, etc., the research team finally dwindled to a hard core of the current authors.

The entire research group became familiar with the existing literature through a thorough discussion and an attempted interpretation of each article. The overview of the literature on depression presented in the preceding chapter is by no means complete, nor does it include the repetitive statements that we abstracted from journals and books or the monotonous reiteration of the clinical symptoms of depressions. Yet our time was not wasted because we used each individual symptom culled from these reports for a list of items which will be described later.

The literature did tell us clearly that the syndrome of depression has become a stereotype, that the theoretical discussions concerning the psychodynamics of depression have created another stereotype, and, finally, that countless questions need to be posed and answered. We list below some of these questions with no hope or promise of answering them all, but to demonstrate, for the sake of completeness, the extent to which clinical psychiatric research is needed.

THE QUESTIONS

For the objectives of our own investigations we asked ourselves the following crucial questions:

I. *On what basis may we say that this person is depressed?*
    A. On the basis of our data can we discern meaningful subgroups under the general heading of Depression?
        1. Are there affective, behavioral, and, if possible, dynamic differences between these groups?
        2. Are there some similarities among all groups that relate them to each other?
    B. What are the characteristics that seem specifically related to Depression or the Depressive Process?
        1. Characteristics or qualities which are essential and pathognomonic.

2. Characteristics or qualities which are frequently seen but are not necessarily essential.
3. Characteristics or qualities which occur sporadically and which do not seem essential but which may help us to define and delineate types or subgroups.

C. Do we find that the diagnosis of depression as used in this study is too inclusive or too exclusive and that further refinement can be made from our observations?

II. *Why did this person become depressed at this particular time?*

A. Can we identify the crucial experience which seems to have precipitated the reaction? This includes both external and internal experiences.
B. What has been the probable essential meaning of this crucial experience to the individual?
C. Can we understand the current reaction in relation to the kind of person this individual is or has been?
    1. The dynamic operations that have maintained his or her equilibrium up to the point of this specific experience.
    2. The specific dynamic operations and defenses which have been called into play, eventually leading to the clinical reaction.
D. Can we get some evidence about the genetic and developmental origins of the current disequilibrium? About the personality development prior to the specific precipitant?
E. Can we distinguish significant or meaningful groups on the basis of the precipitating situation?
F. Where does depression fit in the psychic economy of the individual? Is it a defense against a still more basic anxiety or is it a primary feeling against which other defenses are erected?

Essentially we hoped to describe a large group of depressed patients with an end to delineating the phenomena of depression, asking ourselves whether we could differentiate subgroups within the larger entity that had some behavioral, dynamic, or structural characteristics that would set them apart. We hoped to be able to discern similarities and differences in our patients that might throw light on the complex problem of the depressive process and its clinical variations.

THE TECHNIQUE

Because we were engaged in an empirical research, we could not rely on depth interviews nor on the contents of psychotherapeutic or psychonanalytic sessions. We knew that we would have to observe and interview our subjects intensively. Therefore, for the investigations we decided to use a detailed outline of questions not only derived from the literature but also culled from our combined clinical experiences.

We tried to cover as much as possible of the patient's life history, mental status, and genetic development, and paid particular attention to the development of the present illness. The outline in Table 1 was used as a semistructured guide for the interviewers, who were expected to look for and obtain as much of this information as possible from each patient. We realized that this was an overambitious attempt, yet worthy of a trial, since it was important to know, as we soon did, the extent of information that could be obtained from our techniques.

TABLE 1

AN OUTLINE OF QUESTIONS FOR THE INTERVIEWING AND
OBSERVING OF DEPRESSED PATIENTS

I. On What Basis May We Say That This Person Is Depressed?

A. General Manner and Appearance

1. Impressions as to cooperation, activity, expression,
   relatability
2. Speech
3. Reactions to interviewer
4. Orientation
5. Memory

B. Affect during illness; if possible establish sequence of changing
   affects and establish predominate affect at time of examination

1. Sadness
2. Shame
3. Guilt
4. Helplessness-powerlessness
5. Hopelessness
6. Hopefullness
7. Feelings of loss of esteem
8. Anxiety
9. Boredom
10. Feelings of ambivalence
11. Absence of reported or experienced affect
12. Surges of affect
13. General moodiness
14. Elation
15. Heightened perception or changes in intensity of quality of
    perception
16. Changes in sexual feelings
17. Anger (directed outward or inward)
18. Feelings of going to pieces
19. Loneliness
20. Diurnal variations in affects

C. Thought Processes

1. Confused
2. Retarded
3. Accelerated

(Continued)

28

TABLE 1 *(Continued)*

4. Disorganized
5. Impairment of concentration
6. Indecision

D. Thought Content and Ideation

1. Self-accusation
2. Depersonalization
3. Delusions (nature of delusion)
4. Hallucinations
5. Suicidal Preoccupation
6. Derealization
7. Predominate preoccupations

E. Psychomotor activity

1. Retardation
2. Acceleration
3. Posturing (face, body)
4. Restlessness
5. Changes of activity during illness

F. General Behavior

1. General description of social behavior on nursing unit and in occupational therapy
2. Level of regression
3. Eating behavior
4. Sleeping behavior

G. Somatic symptoms

1. Anorexia—bulimia
2. Insomnia
3. Constipation
4. Headache
5. Dry mouth—bitter taste
6. Changes in hair; sebacious secretion; change in color
7. Weight loss
8. Skin changes (secretions, color)
9. Somatic delusions
10. Include any significant findings from physical examination
    a. blood-pressure—pulse
    b. salivary secretion changes

(Continued)

TABLE 1 *(Continued)*

    c. general physical abnormalities
    d. 24-hour urine volume

II. Why Did This Person Become Depressed at This Particular Time?

  A. Identification of the precipitating experiences

    1. Specific and localized time of onset related by patient or informant to specific experiences
      a. seasonal reactions
      b. anniversary reactions
    2. Change in patient's external relationships, either suddenly or gradually
    3. Internal changes which may be perceived or experienced at some level as constituting a loss or threat
    4. Also consider some of the areas suggested under IIB in attempting to identify the precipitant since the identification and the meaning are interrelated

  B. What seems to be the most probably predominate meaning of this experience to the individual?

    1. The patient's direct statements as to what this experience meant
    2. Specific areas to be looked for as possibilities:
      a. Failure
        (1) of performance
        (2) realization that a specific goal will not be reached
        (3) in competitive situations
        (4) in fantasy
      b. Success
      c. Unexpected awareness of aggressive tendencies
      d. Loss of real object
      e. Loss or devaluation of important object with consequent loss of love
      f. Reaction to shame or guilt over wishes to regress which may approach awareness
      g. Satisfactions minimal with excessive frustrations so that any added frustration precipitates a clinical reaction
      h. Disappointment in mother or mother figure

(Continued)

TABLE 1 *(Continued)*

  i. Physical depletion
  j. Internal changes
    (1) aging
    (2) specific disease, i.e. unconscious perception of illness, such as malignancy

C. Can we understand the current reaction in relation to the pre-morbid personality?

  1. Characteristics of the premorbid personality (with formulation of major dynamics)
    a. General description of interpersonal relationships: deep, relatively superficial, marginal, isolated, distant. Attitudes towards parents, siblings, spouse, friends
    b. Attitudes toward people
    c. More general attitudes; how does he regard the world as a place to live
      (1) hostile
      (2) friendly
      (3) providing
      (4) frustrating
    d. Self-concepts; identifications
    e. Characterization of object relationships (related to (a)); are objects seen as sources of supply; or aggression? Are there fairly mature and realistic attitudes?
    f. Sexual attitudes and activities
    g. Predominate mood states
      (1) generally happy and optimistic
      (2) generally depressed
      (3) chronic anger
      (4) hopeful
    h. Predominate defensive patterns and reactions to stress (how is this handled?); also define what is defended against
      (1) obsessive-compulsive
      (2) phobic and counterphobic mechanisms
      (3) reaction formation
      (4) projection
      (5) denial
      (6) somatic symptoms
      (7) previous depressions
      (8) do "oral" mechanisms and relationships predominate? *(Continued)*

TABLE 1 *(Continued)*

i. School record and performance
j. Work record and performances; work relationships
k. Somatic illness
l. Somatic symptoms
m. Fantasy material
  (1) early memories
  (2) dreams and associations
2. What are the specific dynamic and defensive operations called into play in the emergency?
  a. Reported anxiety, discomfort, or other painful affect
  b. Specific record of sequence of events leading to the depression
    (1) stress
    (2) anxiety
    (3) somatic symptoms—insomnia, etc.
    (4) invoking of other defenses:
      (a) increased compulsive activity
      (b) increased obsessive rumination
      (c) reinforcement of reaction formation
      (d) development of phobic or counterphobic reactions
      (e) attempts at denial and incorporation
      (f) self-abusive behavior
      (g) regression
      (h) projection
      (i) others (mania, elation, hypochondriacal, etc.)
    (5) failure of other defenses and clinical depression with hospitalization
    (6) secondary gains
  c. Is the reaction characteristic of other emergency reactions?
  d. Is there a specific vulnerability?
  e. Has depression been characteristic in this individual?

D. Can we obtain evidence about the genetic origins of the premorbid personality and about the specific present reaction? (secured from someone who has personal information—parent or sibling, etc.)

  1. Somatic differences at birth—deformity, prematurity, oxygen lack, obstetrical injury
  2. Newborn characteristics—degree of activity, feeding demands, etc.

(Continued)

TABLE 1 *(Continued)*

3. Childhood illness
4. Parental attitudes (both from parent and patient)
5. Specific family constellation
   a. parents and relationship between them
   b. siblings
   c. other people present in the household
6. Estimation of mother-child relationship early in life
   (where possible)
   a. satisfactions or dissatisfactions on part of mother
   b. separations and reasons for them
   c. feeding situation—breast, bottle, weaning
7. Development of the child
   a. crawling, walking, talking, etc.
   b. toilet training
   c. masturbation—parental attitudes; patient's reported
      feelings
   d. discipline
   e. school development—any symptoms in this area
8. Development of specific symptoms in childhood
   a. tantrums
   b. nail-biting
   c. nightmares
   d. phobias
   e. eating disturbances
9. Development during latency and problems in this area
   a. acting-out behavior
   b. somatic symptoms
   c. independence-dependence
10. Development during adolescence
    a. increase in sexual feelings; masturbation and feelings
       about this
    b. relation to parents as patient matures
    c. sexual experience; age and reported feelings
    d. choice of profession or vocation
    e. length of education—relations in school with teachers
       and peers
11. Work history
    a. age when began to work
    b. job record
       (1) holds one job for a long time
       (2) drifts from job to job

(Continued)

TABLE 1 *(Continued)*

12. If a parent, attitude toward children and feelings around marriage and parenthood

E. Socio-cultural factors

F. Vital Statistics
1. Name
2. Age
3. Sex
4. Marital status
5. Present family structure
6. Education
7. Occupation
8. Religion
9. Social Class (education, income, neighborhood)
10. Race
11. Ethnic group
12. Military experience
13. Major illness

~~~~~~~~~~~~~~~~~~~~~~~~~~~~~~~~~~~~~~~

CHAPTER 3

Methodology of the
Pilot Study

HAVING DECIDED TO TAKE A "FRESH LOOK" AT THE phenomena of depression and after outlining what we would look for, our next task was to develop suitable *methods* of looking. Since we were primarily interested in behavior, our operations could not be conducted during psychotherapeutic or psychoanalytic interviews because direct observations of behavior under these circumstances are limited, regressions are facilitated, and deficiencies are emphasized to the exclusion of assets. We also left open a formal definition of depression on which to base our choice of subjects, since one of our goals in the research was to ascertain: "On what basis may we say that a person is depressed?" Thus we avoided the logical fallacy of defining in advance the phenomena we were studying. The word *depression* never appears in our descriptions of patients nor as an item in any of our trait lists.

SELECTION OF SUBJECTS

Subjects were selected at random from the roster of patients admitted to the Institute for Psychosomatic and Psychiatric Research and Training of Michael Reese Hospital. We shall refer to this institution henceforth by its widely used abbreviation of PPI.

We did not concern ourselves whether the patient had prior depressive episodes or whether this was his first admission to PPI. The criterion for inclusion in the study was simply the *diagnosis* of "Depression" or "Depressive Reaction" as the predominant presenting problem by *both* the attending psychiatrist and the resident psychiatrist who admitted the patient. In fact, throughout this book the term *depression* refers to a syndrome included in our current classification of psychiatric diseases and *not* to a symptom or an affect. We deliberately left the criteria this broad so as to include a wide range of patients in our sample, thus increasing the possibility of picking up different groups. Later we shall discuss how we dealt with data concerning those patients admitted as depressions but who after diagnostic study turned out to be otherwise classified on their discharge from the hospital.

COMPILATION OF DATA

Patients were observed and interviewed to obtain as much information as possible corresponding to the outline given in the previous chapter. Interviews were continued until it became apparent to the investigators that no further information could be obtained without altering the structure of the experiment by giving suggestions or making interpretations to the subjects.

In addition, whenever possible one or more relatives were interviewed to obtain additional information. These included predominantly husbands and wives of patients, parents, and other people who were close to them.

Each patient was interviewed by a member of the research group, while another member watched and listened to as many interviews as possible behind a one-way mirror. Thus, at least two members of the group had direct experience with almost every patient. After each interview, these two members of the research group discussed the data to decide upon areas that had been overlooked or insufficiently explored. These were then the subject matter of a subsequent interview, until both investigators were satisfied that the information was as complete as possible. Since some patients were under the care of psychiatrists who prescribed various forms of somatotherapy, investigation was stopped when they were started on shock treatment, usually after two or three interviews, and the protocol was considered completed at that point.

After completion of data-gathering from the patient and relatives, a complete descriptive report was prepared by the interviewer for presentation to the entire research group. At this meeting questions were raised, and, if necessary and the patient was still available, he was interviewed again to obtain the additional information.

As the pilot program progressed, we scanned the reports about each subject and tried to compare and contrast them in order to establish categories and relationships, but this proved impossible. After much discussion, we concluded that data from more than two or three patients could not be scanned at one time, and even this number only with great difficulty, because, as a result of our attempt to describe the individual and specific characteristics of each person as completely as possible, we had too much information.

We were thus in the position of having extensive information about the phenomena of depression in a pilot group of 21 patients and reluctantly concluding that it was necessary to use statistical methods in order to compare them.

STATISTICAL METHOD

The statistical problem was twofold. On the one hand we had to change the data from case reports into some form that could be handled statistically, and secondly we had to find a method for analyzing the data in a manner that would be useful. Since we were analyzing a mass of behavioral information from which we hoped to extract some patterning or grouping, the method of factor analysis seemed the most effective technique. To convert the data into a form which could be utilized for factor analysis, we chose after considerable statistical advice the Q-sort technique, which, in spite of some limitations such as forcing a difficult choice, seemed most directly applicable to our material.

Processing the Data

Along with the advantages which Q-technique offered in our pilot studies, we were aware that some disadvantages might be present and that some cautions would have to be heeded. An important caution is that, before raters can sensibly make Q-sorts and before the results can be meaningfully analyzed, all of the items must be from some common frame of reference.

The Q-sort involves the preparation of a series of cards, each one carrying a characteristic which describes the process or individual under consideration and about which quantitative judgments can be made. The statements about the traits themselves are not quantitative, since the Q-sort elicits the degree to which the traits are judged to participate in the depressive syndrome.

These cards are sorted into thirteen piles (0 to 12). Those traits that are most characteristic are placed in Pile 12, and those that are most *un*characteristic placed in Pile 0. Traits about which little is known or which are of lesser importance in characterizing the subjects are placed in successively decreasing or increasing piles toward the center. Pile 6, which is directly in the center, thus contains those traits which are neither characteristic nor uncharacteristic for a given patient, and these traits accordingly play little role in the subsequent statistical results.

For this technique it is necessary that the traits be numerically distributed on an approximately normal curve. Thus Piles 12 and 0 might each contain two traits, Piles 11 and 1 four traits, Piles 10 and 2 five traits, etc. This has the effect of forcing choices upon the rater which he may find difficult to make, but the result is to construct a pattern of traits describing some aspect of a particular subject which can be treated statistically and, in turn, compared and contrasted with other such descriptions (Figs. 1 and 2).

Converting the Data

Having decided upon a data-processing method that would allow the kind of comparisons we were interested in making, it became necessary to convert our data from the prose form of statements and observations into quantifiable characterizations. The first task was to prepare a list of characteristics, a "trait universe," that would be sufficiently broad to allow meaningful discriminations and at the same time concise enough to be usable. As we worked on this, we realized that we had descriptions which had to do with feelings, concerns, experiences, somatic sensations, and dreams on the one hand and, on the other hand, data that described behavior as it was viewed by an external observer. It was difficult to combine these into a single "trait universe," so we decided to construct two separate lists and to conduct two separate Q-sorts.

TRAIT LISTS

We used our original protocol as a basis and then reviewed the written reports on all 21 of our patients, extracting from these those characteristics or traits that we could describe and quantify. At first we had several hundred traits in each category, which we were able after much discussion to condense into 111 traits dealing with "feelings and concerns" (Table 2) and into 87 traits (Table 3) describing characteristics entitled "current behavior."

OTHER CHECK LISTS

We still found ourselves with kinds of information that could not be handled in this manner. Somatic symptoms could not be put in the same category and described as more or less characteristic of a particular patient. Headaches, for example, might be a prominent symptom and quantifiable as to frequency and intensity, but

Figure 1

"Feelings and Concerns" Score Sheet

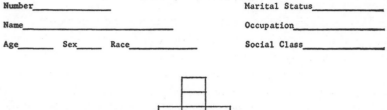

Number_____   Marital Status_____

Name_____   Occupation_____

Age_____ Sex_____ Race_____   Social Class_____

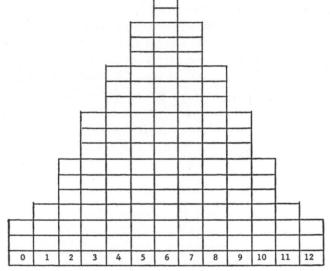

could not properly be conceptualized as "characteristic" or "uncharacteristic" of a person in the same way as feelings, attitudes,
and concerns. These then were appended as a "symptom check
list," and the raters were asked to make rough quantitative judgments about the importance of a particular symptom on a three-
point rating scale (Table 4).

Likewise we elicited information concerning frequency and type
of dreams whose manifest content ranged so widely that categories
were difficult to establish. However, we set up an arbitrary list

Figure 2

"Current Behavior" Score Sheet

Number_____

Name_____

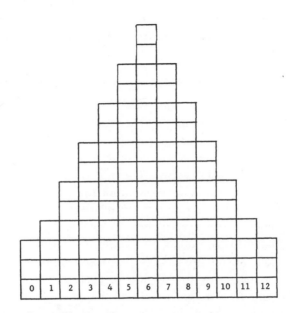

of 40 types to be used as a check list for each patient, without much hope that significant. information would result (Table 5).

In our interviewing we focused on the precipitating experiences or, better expressed, significant feelings or events occurring antecedent to the first indication of depression. Even in recording our observations it was apparent that several situations or events seemed equally concerned in disturbing the patient's equilibrium. Our preliminary discussions revealed our difficulties in making decisions concerning the significance of a wide range of premorbid events and of choosing a reasonable time limit between event and onset of the depression syndrome. Nevertheless, we devised a 65-item check list to include what seemed to be the most frequent and precipitating experiences occurring within a year prior to the illness, and we included the significant persons who might be involved with the patient (Table 6). We then added a list of 18 general meanings which could be abstracted from the actual events in the hope that a sufficient number of common meanings could then be useful for some form of categorization of types of onset (Table 7).

Discussion of the Use of the Check Lists

A glance at the tables (2-7) demonstrating our six check lists will suffice to indicate that they contain a wide range of traits constructed by us from information in the literature, from our own personal experiences, and abstracted from the reports on the subjects of the pilot study. The words and phrases used are not necessarily direct quotations from the patients' utterances; rather they have been translated into relatively jargon-free nontechnical language clearly agreed upon by us and we hope equally understandable by any other psychiatric investigator. Working together enabled the researchers to understand thoroughly what behavior or statement was appropriate for each trait item.

It should also be understood that there is a range or scale of objectivity–subjectivity within the six check lists. The current behavior list is a description of actually observed behavior and should be the most objective. The lists of symptoms, dream types, and precipitating events contain items directly reported by the patients. They simply state: "I have such and such pain or distress" or "I had the following dream" or "Just before I got depressed, such and such happened." The meanings of the so-called precipitating events were abstracted from the patients' accounts and interpreted according to the 18 general meanings which we considered might be reasonably interpreted.

Finally we turn to the feelings and concerns check list, which is a combination objective–subjective scale. All the traits in this list are obtained from the subjects' verbal communications and verbal behavior. Some traits are exact reproductions of the patients' statements, such as "I feel at the end of my rope" or "I feel hopeless" or "I feel lonely," etc. Others are interpretations or inferences made by the interviewer from the patient's verbal behavior, such as "Anger that is present is attached to a reasonable object" or "Gets much secondary gain from illness" or "Has unrealistic fear of cancer," etc.

Close scrutiny of the feelings and concerns list will, however, indicate that the vast majority of traits can be (and have been) expressed directly by the patient who spontaneously complains or responds to the interviewer's interrogations. However, the list is also a fertile field for interpretations of feelings from intonations, paralingual grunts, sighs, etc., gestures, and total behavior. There can be no doubt that this check list permits both direct objective recording and inferences, a fact which later rose to plague us.

SUMMARY

In the pilot study 21 patients admitted to PPI with the diagnosis of depression were interviewed and observed by a psychiatrist who was observed and overheard by another psychiatrist from behind a one-way screen. Discussions between the two psychiatrists and repeated interviews were conducted to elicit as much information as possible. A trait list of 111 feelings and concerns and 87 current behavior traits was Q-sorted. Four check lists were also employed consisting of 59 symptoms, 40 dream types, 65 precipitating events, and 18 meanings of precipitating events.

TABLE 2

FEELINGS AND CONCERNS TRAIT LIST

1. Concerned with death or dying
2. Feels "at end of rope"
3. Denies experiencing any pleasure
4. Gets much secondary gain from illness
5. Feels he (she) brought illness on self
6. Concerned with suffering caused others
7. Feels a failure
8. Has a fear of mental disintegration
9. Complains of feeling dirty
10. Complains of not being able to experience things as before
11. Considers self as lazy
12. Feelings are dominated by sadness and "blueness"
13. Little sadness experienced
14. Shame is experienced
15. Some shame over being ill, in contrast to shame as part of illness
16. Guilt feelings experienced
17. Guilt feelings reported for the past but not for present
18. Feels helpless and powerless
19. Feels hopeless
20. Feels self unworthy
21. Feels unloved
22. Feels loss of esteem by others
23. Feels he (she) can never return to former life
24. Has feeling of tenseness
25. Experiences free anxiety
26. Has anxiety toward particular concerns
27. Feels constantly fatigued
28. Feels more energetic than before
29. Boredom is a predominant feeling
30. Interests experienced as broader and more active than before
31. Feels ambivalent toward important personal issues
32. Experiences sudden surges of intense affect
33. Experiences moodiness
34. Professes to have little or no feelings
35. Feels elated
36. Feels excited
37. Feels better now than previously
38. Feels worse now than previously
39. Experiences rapidly changing feeling
40. Has sense of changing perception—things look different in some undefinable way

(Continued)

44

TABLE 2 *(Continued)*

41. Experiences usual sexual feelings
42. Decreased sexual feelings and interests
43. Increased sexual feelings and interests
44. Concern over waning sexual capacity
45. Concern over waning sexual interest
46. Concern over increasing sexual interest
47. Anger is experienced
48. Anger that is present attached to reasonable object
49. Anger that is present attached to unreasonable object
50. Has changing feelings during day
51. Feels lonely
52. Feels closer to people now than before
53. Feels more distant from people now than before
54. Feels burdened by demands of others
55. Wants to cry much of the time
56. Feels unable to cry now
57. Feels envious of others
58. Feels bland
59. Feels as though things will get better in near future
60. Can laugh at times
61. Alternates between feelings of cheerfulness and sadness
62. Feels relieved after hospitalization
63. Feels more upset after hospitalization
64. Feels "jittery"
65. Concerned with "getting even" with others
66. Fears that he (she) might hurt someone else
67. Optimistic
68. Mind in the past—cannot think about life ahead
69. Experiences tension as somatic symptoms rather than in relation to social environment
70. Attributes all problems to somatic difficulties rather than to personal adjustment
71. Feels that condition will grow steadily worse
72. Feels that he (she) is becoming ugly and unattractive
73. Feels that illness was brought on by others
74. Feels loss of interest in "oral satisfactions"—food, drink, and smoking
75. Has increased concern for "oral satisfactions"—food, drink, and smoking
76. Expresses much concern for the welfare of family and friends
77. Has an increased interest in religion
78. Feels guilt for not assuming family/and/or job responsibilities

(Continued)

TABLE 2 *(Continued)*

79. Feels confused
80. Feels that he (she) is being brave in bearing troubles
81. Feels that illness was precipitated by recent events
82. Feels that illness is due to long history of personal events
83. Feels that illness was brought on by specific event or trauma
84. Credits illness to excessive family and/or job responsibility
85. Feels that illness would be relieved by the solving of certain "material" problems—money, job, housing, etc.
86. Feels that family and/or friends can be counted on to help in solving problems
87. Expresses distrust of people in general—feels people will let him (her) down
88. Expresses resolutions to change, act different, "do better"
89. Ashamed of illness—hopes that friends will not learn about condition
90. Concerned about internal disintegration
91. Concerned with aging and lessening vigor
92. Considers self clumsy and awkward
93. Concerned with making up for wrongs to others
94. Has sense of danger
95. Contemplates "flight" from scene, move to new location
96. Concerned with material loss—money, property, etc.
97. Feels he (she) is being persecuted
98. Feels old and dried-out
99. Feels hopeful about getting better
100. Feels unlovable
101. Feels confused and disorganized
102. Feels his (her) thinking is slowed
103. Feels he (she) thinks much quicker than before
104. Feels unable to make decisions
105. Feels unable to concentrate
106. Wishes to act impulsively
107. Feels unable to act
108. Has ideas of committing suicide
109. Wishes to hurt others
110. Preoccupied with physical symptoms
111. Has unrealistic fear of cancer

TABLE 3

CURRENT BEHAVIOR TRAIT LIST

1. Isolated and withdrawn
2. Tries to impress others with own talents
3. Exhibitionistic
4. Regards other people as a source of help
5. Is interested in how others react to him (her)
6. Asks many questions
7. Avoids looking at others
8. Wants to learn about other people's lives and work
9. Misunderstands the purposes and intentions of others
10. Expresses appreciation for interest and understanding
11. Friendly
12. Confides easily to others
13. Is relieved to be able to talk with someone
14. Relates in a distant and guarded manner
15. Dresses neatly
16. Dresses inappropriately
17. Seductive
18. Careless and unbecoming posture
19. Restless and fidgety
20. Inattentive and distracted
21. Frightened of others
22. Overtly hostile
23. Attempts to depreciate others
24. Anxious to please
25. Tries to advise others
26. Wants other people to evaluate his (her) condition
27. Clings to others
28. Tries to lead conversation to avoid embarrassing topics
29. Belittles own problems—describes them as transitory
30. Denies need for help
31. Considerable pressure to talk
32. Reluctant to talk
33. Becomes more communicative as relationships develop
34. Becomes less communicative as relationships develop
35. Appears holding back, as though to avoid strong emotions
36. Speech is mumbled and slurred
37. Speech is accelerated
38. Alert and responsive
39. Avoids answering questions directly
40. Tries to sidetrack conversations to irrelevant topics
41. Recognizes need for help

(Continued)

TABLE 3 *(Continued)*

42. Shows "sickening sweet" ingratiating behavior
43. Makes an effort to be cheerful even if feelings are different
44. Shows humor
45. Expresses willingness to cooperate with others in mutual projects
46. Attempts self-diagnosis, explaining own problems in an intellectualized manner
47. Apathetic
48. Eager to terminate conversations
49. Concern with own problems prevents the understanding of what other people say
50. Reluctant to terminate conversations with others
51. Concerned with burdening or boring others
52. Expresses appreciation for the attention of others
53. Warm and personable
54. Engrossment in own feelings lowers awareness of the presence of others
55. Fluctuates between an apparent confidence in and suspicion of others
56. Changes topic of conversation frequently
57. Discusses "false problems" as cover-up for more basic issues
58. Claims to receive considerable help from talking with others
59. Makes an effort to be composed and dignified
60. Asks others to clarify questions and remarks
61. Respectful and polite
62. Tries to impress others with severity of own problems
63. Talks only when spoken to
64. Languid and "overrelaxed"
65. Irritated and impatient when asked questions
66. Clarifies own remarks considerably, as though to give very precise information
67. Inquires about the purpose and intentions of others
68. Tries to be witty and charming
69. Changes posture and sitting position frequently
70. Inappropriate facial expressions
71. Cries or sobs in presence of others
72. Tries to lead others
73. Tries to help others
74. Makes excessive demands on others
75. Makes dramatic gestures
76. Tries to calm and reassure others
77. Acts as though others are obligated to help him (her)
78. Maintains "forced" smile

(Continued)

TABLE 3 *(Continued)*

79. Exaggerated facial expressions
80. Accepts gifts readily
81. Critical of the habits and manner of others
82. Rapid changes from friendliness to anger
83. Makes an effort to agree with others
84. Treats others as social inferiors
85. Generous with own possessions
86. More communicative with men than women
87. Switches activities frequently

TABLE 4

SOMATIC SYMPTOMS CHECK LIST

Rate the patient on each of the following symptoms. If the condition is not present write nothing in the space to the left. Write a "1" if the condition is present in only a slight degree. Write a "2" if the condition is marked, or moderately severe. Write a "3" if the condition is very strongly in evidence, or severe. Unless the item states otherwise, the patient is to be rated as he is at present.

_____   1. Increased appetite

_____   2. Decreased appetite

_____   3. Difficulty in getting to sleep

_____   4. Wakeful during night

_____   5. Constipation (since illness)

_____   6. Constipation (before illness)

_____   7. Frequent urination

_____   8. Headaches (since illness)

_____   9. Headaches (before illness)

_____ 10. Dryness of mouth

_____ 11. Bad taste in mouth

_____ 12. Change in hair texture and dryness

_____ 13. Change in hair color

_____ 14. Dryness of skin

_____ 15. Change in skin color

_____ 16. Weight loss

_____ 17. Weight gain

_____ 18. Preoccupation with physical symptoms which have no organic basis

_____ 19. Delusions about body function

_____ 20. Experiences tension as a somatic symptom referred to specific organ or area

_____ 21. Choking sensation

_____ 22. Unrealistic fear of cancer

(Continued)

TABLE 4 *(Continued)*

_____ 23. Recurrent abdominal pain

_____ 24. Abdominal distension

_____ 25. Belching

_____ 26. Diarrhea

_____ 27. Nausea

_____ 28. Dizzyness

_____ 29. Somatic residual illness

_____ 30. Specific somatic illness

_____ 31. Pain in jaw muscles

_____ 32. Requires sedation to sleep

_____ 33. Diminished appetite

_____ 34. Objects to hospital food
(compared with food outside)

_____ 35. Sensation of hunger, but not able to eat

_____ 36. Unusual posturing

_____ 37. Assumes fetal position

_____ 38. Wrings hands

_____ 39. Strikes self with hands

_____ 40. Change in voice quality

_____ 41. Sweating

_____ 42. Picks at self or clothing

_____ 43. Delusions

_____ 44. Hallucinations

_____ 45. Suspicious of others

_____ 46. Feelings of depersonalization

_____ 47. Feelings of derealization

_____ 48. Disorganized thinking

_____ 49. Confusion

_____ 50. Thought processes slowed

(Continued)

TABLE 4 *(Continued)*

_____ 51. Thought processes accelerated

_____ 52. Thought processes circumstantial

_____ 53. Thought processes tangential

_____ 54. Preoccupation with details

_____ 55. Impaired concentration

_____ 56. Blocking in train of thought

_____ 57. Attention impaired

_____ 58. Distractable

_____ 59. Diminished ability to communicate

TABLE 5

DREAM CHECK LIST

Make a check mark beside those statements which describe the patient's dreams.

_____ 1. Has frightening dreams

_____ 2. Has pleasurable dreams

_____ 3. Dreams of being pursued

_____ 4. Dreams of pursuing someone else

_____ 5. Dreams of falling

_____ 6. Dreams of flying

_____ 7. Dreams of things (e.g., walls) closing in

_____ 8. Dreams of murder or mayhem

_____ 9. Dreams of suicide

_____ 10. Dreams of death or being dead

_____ 11. Dreams of being a child

_____ 12. Dreams which involve solving a problem which is never solved

_____ 13. Dreams in which a problem is solved

_____ 14. Dreams of returning to important places

_____ 15. Dreams contain people

_____ 16. Dreams contain animals

_____ 17. Dreams contain monsters

_____ 18. Dreams in which there are no animate objects

_____ 19. Dreams in which inanimate objects act as though alive

_____ 20. Dreams of being immobilized

_____ 21. Dreams of being in a moving vehicle

_____ 22. Dreams of protecting someone or something

_____ 23. Dreams of being protected by someone

_____ 24. Has pleasant dream involving fulfillment of conscious wishes

(Continued)

TABLE 5 *(Continued)*

_____ 25. Dreams of being helped by others

_____ 26. Dreams of helping others

_____ 27. Dreams of needing help and being refused

_____ 28. Dreams of someone being ill or hurt

_____ 29. Dreams of sexual activity

_____ 30. Has world-destructive dreams

_____ 31. Has manifestly cannabalistic dreams

_____ 32. Has dreams of incestuous sexual activity

_____ 33. Dreams are predominately hostile and destructive in character

_____ 34. Dreams show attempts at restitutive processes

_____ 35. Dreams show predominately isolation

_____ 36. Sleepwalking has occurred

_____ 37. No dreams can be obtained

_____ 38. Reports numerous dreams

_____ 39. Dreams are vivid and lifelike

_____ 40. Dreams are nebulous and difficult to recall

TABLE 6

PRECIPITATING EVENTS CHECK LIST

In this section of the check list, you are to indicate significant events in the patient's environment which preceded hospitalization. The rating form is arranged so that you can rate simultaneously the event and the person who experienced the event. For example, if the patient's father committed suicide, this would be indicated in the column under father at row 2.

Events should be indicated whether or not they involve the patient directly. For example, if the patient's son has committed a criminal act, this should be so indicated regardless of whether or not the father participated directly in the crime.

Instead of making only a mark to indicate whether the event occurred or not, you are to make a judgment as to the importance of the event in precipitating the current mental illness:

Write "1" in the proper space if you judge the event to be of only slight importance in precipitating the illness. Write "2" in the space if you judge the event to be of some, but not major, importance in precipitating the illness. Write "3" in the space if you judge the event to be of major importance in precipitating the illness.

Some clarification of terms is needed before you begin. The term "lover" is used to denote either an extramarital relationship or relationship between persons who are both unmarried. The words "business" and "job" are used in the general sense to refer to whatever the person does—profession, trade, or scholarly endeavor.

Event	Person Who Experienced Event													
	Patient	Mother	Father	Spouse	Grandparent	Grandchild	Lover	Sister	Brother	Son	Daughter	Bus. Assoc.	Bus. Superior	Other
1. Death (other than suicide)														
2. Suicide														
3. Attempted suicide with major physical damage														

(Continued)

TABLE 6 *(Continued)*

Event	Patient	Mother	Father	Spouse	Grandparent	Grandchild	Lover	Sister	Brother	Son	Daughter	Bus. Assoc.	Bus. Superior	Other
4. Attempted suicide with only minor physical damage														
5. Chronic illness														
6. Improvement in chronic illness														
7. Critical illness with early recovery														
8. Surgical operation with subsequent disability														
9. Surgical removal of narcissistically important organ														
10. Injury from accident														
11. Negligence brings physical harm to someone														
12. Physical disability														
13. Criminial act														
14. Loss of job														
15. Demotion on job														
16. Promotion on job														
17. Business success														
18. Business failure														
19. Change in work role														
20. Retirement														
21. Vacation														
22. Separation from family														

(Continued)

TABLE 6 *(Continued)*

Event	Patient	Mother	Father	Spouse	Grandparent	Grandchild	Lover	Sister	Brother	Son	Daughter	Bus. Assoc.	Bus. Superior	Other
23. Moved to new residence location														
24. Traumatic sexual experience														
25. Infidelity														
26. New sexual experience														
27. Had socially unacceptable sexual experience														
28. Experienced lessening sexual vigor														
29. Experienced sexual rejection														
30. Heightened sexual interest														
31. Infertility or sterility														
32. Pregnancy														
33. Miscarriage														
34. Induced abortion														
35. Childbirth														
36. Marriage														
37. Divorce														
38. Marital separation														
39. Menopause														
40. Had evidence of aging														
41. Mental Illness (other than patient)														

(Continued)

TABLE 6 *(Continued)*

Event	Patient	Mother	Father	Spouse	Grandparent	Grandchild	Lover	Sister	Brother	Son	Daughter	Bus. Assoc.	Bus. Superior	Other
42. Alcoholism														
43. Loss of goods, money, or property														
44. Financial insecurity														
45. Performs physically aggressive act														
46. Affectionate approach by important person														
47. Expressed affection to important person														
48. Criticized important person														
49. Criticized by important person														
50. Experienced overt hostility														
51. Expressed overt hostility to important person														
52. Participated in important event (celebration, anniversary, etc.)														
53. Confessed previous misgivings to important person														
54. Experienced physical danger														
55. Experienced protracted physical danger														
56. Loss of pet animal														
57. Continuous marital quarrels and arguments														

(Continued)

TABLE 6 *(Continued)*

Event	Patient	Mother	Father	Spouse	Grandparent	Grandchild	Lover	Sister	Brother	Son	Daughter	Bus. Assoc.	Bus. Superior	Other
58. "Makes fool" of self in important situation														
59. General disturbance in environment (noise, distraction, impediments, etc.)														
60. Removed from recreational pursuits, avocation, or hobby														
61. Overwork														
62. Had misdeed exposed														
63. Kept away from home by increasing outside activity														
64. Trouble with in-laws														
65. Changing relationships														

TABLE 7

MEANINGS OF THE PRECIPITATING EVENTS

Below is a list of possible meanings which any of the precipitating events may have had for a patient. In the box below list the number of each precipitating event you have selected as involved in this patient's illness. Next to this put the letter(s) indicating the meaning that you think this event had to the patient.

If you feel that some event meant something which is not listed, then indicate this by the letter Z (Z_1, Z_2, Z_3, etc.) and at the bottom of the page specify the meaning of each item.

Precipitating Event No.	Meaning

Other Meanings:

Z: Z_2:

Z_1: Z_3:

A. Real loss of satisfactions
B. Increased inability to accept satisfactions available
C. Increased awareness of inability to control strong emotions (anger, fear, grief, etc.)
D. Increased awareness of unacceptable thoughts and wishes
E. Loss of self-esteem by patient
F. Diminished esteem of patient for important person
G. Fear of punishment or retaliation
H. Fear of exposure for own misdeeds
I. Increased feeling of social inadequacy
J. Fear of permanent injury
K. Feeling of rejection

(Continued)

60

TABLE 7 *(Continued)*

L. Attempt to form object relationships thwarted
M. Diminished opportunity for dependent gratification
N. Breakdown of defenses
O. Increased concern over "mental imbalance"
P. Awareness of unrealistic character of own goals
Q. Reduction in strength of internal controls
R. Increased self-perception of declining capacity
   (aging, physical dysfunction, loss of attractiveness, etc.)

CHAPTER 4

Results of the Pilot Study

As the statistical analyses of our data from the pilot study were completed and the results studied, a great deal was learned about the pitfalls as well as the possible results of empirical research. In this sense the pilot study was preparatory to the quantitatively larger research to be carried out later with a different design. However, the pilot study had a positive value in that it constituted a separate investigation, the results of which should be compared with those obtained from the second study.

DETERMINING THE RELIABILITY OF THE RESULTS

In our project "reliability" refers to the relative consistency with which patients are rated alike by different raters. If we had four blood-pressure gauges and they generally gave four very different indications of the systolic pressure for patients, we would have little faith in the instruments and would be unwilling to trust their readings in research investigations. For the same reason, if four psychiatrists make ratings (with the Q-sort, for example) of 21 patients, and the trend is for the psychiatrists to agree very little with one another about the cases, then the ratings will probably be of little use in subsequent investigations of the patients. In our studies we frequently made use of the measure of reliability (or agreement) which is called "coefficient alpha." It ranges from 1.00 to .00, with 1.00 meaning perfect reliability and .00 meaning no reliability. Although the required level of the coefficient depends on how the data will be used, most people would agree that, generally speaking, a coefficient as high as .70 is "fair," .80 "good," and .90 "excellent." Obtaining high reliability is not an end in itself, but a prelude to performing research about patients. As is widely known, high reliability does not necessarily mean that ratings provide *valid* descriptions of patients; but if reliability is very low, the ratings as a group cannot be valid or correct in any sense. For these reasons we performed extensive investigation of reliability before using our instruments in substantive studies.

Use of Factor Analysis in the Research

Because in this chapter it will be necessary to refer to some factor-analytic statistical investigations, it is necessary to turn aside for a moment and discuss how factor analysis was used in the research. For those who are not familiar with the technical issues involved, factor analysis is a mathematical procedure for finding groups (or clusters) of items that tend to measure the same thing, and each such group of items is called a "factor." Some of the factors found in this way are what was expected before the analysis was undertaken. In these instances, the advantage of factor analysis is that it provides for a definite test of hypothesized groupings of items. Sometimes the suspected groupings of items do not occur, which indicates that prior conceptions were incorrect. In addition to testing for the presence of suspected groupings of items, factor analysis also provides a means of discovering unsuspected groupings of items. Although we used a variety of factor-analytic techniques in our studies, and the technical details of these may be either obscure or unpalatable to some of our readers, the over-all purposes and results were (1) testing hypotheses about groupings of psychological traits, and (2) discovering unsuspected groupings of traits.

In doing rotations, the attempt is made to locate the reference abilities in such positions that each has a few rather high positive loadings, and many insignificant low loadings. Thus each factor is characterized by a cluster of variables. Occasionally one factor will have several variables with rather high positive loadings and other variables with rather high negative loadings, neither of which can be reduced by rotation. Consequently, this will be denoted as a bipolar factor. Usually the variables which define a bipolar factor are opposite in meaning; for example, if those with the positive loadings tend to describe an extrovert, those with the negative loadings would tend to describe an introvert. In our research, Factor C of the pilot study was the most important factor which was bipolar, having both positive and negative clusters with high loadings.

Factor analysis is mainly an aspect of the tool-making phase of research. After the factors are found, they are given meaning through establishing hypotheses useful for subsequent research. Although we have explored our factors to some extent in those ways, we have not yet carried that research nearly as far as we would have liked. Consequently, we hope that others will borrow our factors and put them to proper uses in studies of psychiatric patients.

Extent of Agreement Among the Rating Psychiatrists

An analysis of the amount of agreement between the four psychiatrists who rated each patient was undertaken for both the feelings and concerns and current behavior sorts. The psychiatrists correlated well with each other on the feelings and concerns list (Table 8) with a coefficient alpha of .81. However, one patient (7) fell below .70 to the level of .64 and was dropped from the

TABLE 8

THE ORDER OF AGREEMENT* WITH WHICH 4 PSYCHIATRISTS RATE 21 PATIENTS

Case Number	Feelings and Concerns Sample	Current Behavior Sample
1	.85	.81
2	.90	.81
3	.80	.71
4	.84	.69
5	.89	.76
6	.83	.78
7	.64	.55
8	.85	.75
9	.76	.62
10	.77	.70
11	.72	.53
12	.83	.72
13	.87	.73
14	.82	.70
15	.85	.64
16	.73	.80
17	.84	.82
18	.79	.61
19	.72	.76
20	.79	.76
21	.84	.70
Average	.81	.71

*The amount of agreement is shown for each case by coefficient alpha. A number less than .70 represents an unsatisfactory amount of agreement; .80 is high agreement; and .90 is very high agreement.

TABLE 9

THE ORDER OF AGREEMENT FOR THE FEELINGS AND CONCERNS TRAITS AS APPLIED TO 21 PATIENTS

Rank	Trait	Rank	Trait	Rank	Trait
1	33	38	20	76	53
2	40	39	18	77	91
3	19	40	55	78	17
4	41	41	78	79	29
5	77	42	11	80	71
6	104	43	98	81	38
7	65	44	100	82	96
8	2	45	68	83	25
9	87	46	39	84	3
10	45	47	30	85	54
11	80	48	85	86	76
12	22	49	27	87	61
13	46	50	21	88	75
14	42	51	50	89	23
15	72	52	57	90	32
16	111	53	62	91	58
17	9	54	97	92	94
18	10	55	110	93	73
19	51	56	70	94	90
20	24	58	101	95	15
21	43	59	35	96	83
22	103	60	107	97	89
23	108	61	93	98	6
24	44	62	81	99	36
25	82	63	12	100	69
26	109	64	28	101	56
27	8	65	49	102	60
28	7	66	106	103	67
29	92	67	79	104	34
30	52	68	74	105	4
31	105	69	63	106	37
32	31	70	48	107	59
33	14	71	95	108	13
34	64	72	26	109	99
35	88	73	84	110	5
36	16	74	66	111	47
37	102	75	1		

TABLE 10

THE ORDER OF AGREEMENT FOR THE CURRENT BEHAVIOR TRAITS AS APPLIED TO 21 PATIENTS

Rank	Trait	Rank	Trait	Rank	Trait
1	85	$30\frac{1}{2}$	49	59	21
2	60	$30\frac{1}{2}$	77	60	17
3	6	32	28	61	18
4	86	33	70	62	71
5	56	34	54	63	68
6	72	35	15	64	78
7	80	36	20	65	65
8	8	37	51	66	81
9	7	38	63	67	53
10	5	39	40	68	66
11	19	40	48	69	36
12	84	41	13	70	62
13	69	42	73	71	14
14	25	43	10	72	58
15	31	44	35	73	82
16	41	45	27	74	3
17	9	46	2	75	38
18	4	47	52	76	44
19	87	48	59	77	75
20	57	49	79	78	64
21	26	50	46	79	74
$22\frac{1}{2}$	55	51	32	80	30
$22\frac{1}{2}$	83	52	37	81	12
24	16	53	61	82	43
25	24	54	23	83	29
$26\frac{1}{2}$	39	55	50	84	1
$26\frac{1}{2}$	67	56	11	85	47
28	76	57	33	86	22
29	42	58	34	87	45

remainder of the study. Although the better intelligence tests usually have an alpha of .90 it is generally accepted that .70 indicates fair reliability in an investigation of this kind. In our study all coefficients (except Case 7 above) were above .70, with one reaching as high as .90. From this preliminary analysis it was apparent that our raters could describe patients' feelings and concerns with sufficient accuracy to permit us to proceed with factor analytic studies.

The current behavior ratings were considerably less reliable in that the average coefficient alpha reached only .71. Although this is slightly above the .70 which is usually considered satisfactory we did not consider that factor analysis of this trait universe would be fruitful, although the rank order of the items is important (Table 10).

In addition to the general correlations indicating the degree of reliability we abstracted those specific items concerning which there was most and least agreement among the raters. The orders of agreement for feelings and concerns and for current behavior are given in Tables 9 and 10. The individual items appearing among the ten most and least agreed-upon statements appear in Table 11 and 12.

Agreement seems high on several neutral characteristics that are not apparently related to depression among those that seemed appropriately relevant. On the other hand, there is profound disagreement over a trait such as "anger is experienced" to which the raters were particularly sensitive in view of the presumed relation of aggression and its vicissitudes to depression. Yet, perhaps because of this extra attentiveness, the raters cannot agree as to its presence or extent. The same is true about such attitudes as hopefulness and optimism, although excellent agreement is obtained about moodiness, hopelessness, and distrust. Interesting and important questions about the amounts and kinds of agreement between psychiatrists observing the same phenomena are raised by this preliminary study, to which we will return later.

An analysis was undertaken to determine the predominating characteristics in all of the depressed patients sorted so far. First a composite sort was made for each patient by adding the results of every psychiatrist's sort of that patient. Then an over-all composite for 21 patients was made by adding their separate composites. Over-all composites were obtained separately for the feeling and concerns sample and the current behavior sample. These are listed respectively in Tables 13 and 14. Looking at Table 13, Item 19 (feels hopeless), is the most characteristic of all 21 patients. An interpretation of the two profiles could only be made with caution because at that time we did not yet know how typical the composite was for the 21 cases; this was determined by subsequent factor analysis. Furthermore, it is statistically unsafe to interpret more than 10 or 20 most characteristic and 10 or 20 least characteristic items.

THE DISCREPANCY BETWEEN THE RELIABILITY OF RATINGS OF FEELINGS AND CONCERNS TRAITS AND CURRENT BEHAVIOR TRAITS

The separate composite sorts for patients were sufficiently reliable to procede with the planned factor analysis of feelings and concerns. The findings so far were clear-cut and interesting and gave promise for a fruitful program of continued research. Although our major purpose was to study depressions, the results indicated that some interesting things could be learned as well about how psychiatrists make clinical judgments. We had a solid and extensive set of findings on the amount and kinds of clinical agreement among psychiatrists.

After studying the data concerning agreement among psychiatric raters we became concerned with the unreliability of the descriptions of behavioral aspects of depression in contrast with the reliability of our interpretive judgments about the patient's internal feelings and concerns. Questions of reliability are of tremendous importance in a study of this kind before we can trust the results. Therefore

TABLE 11

THE 10 MOST AND 10 LEAST AGREED-ON STATEMENTS IN THE FEELINGS AND CONCERNS LIST

Rank	*Most* Trait	
1	33	Experiences moodiness
2	40	Has sense of changing perception—things look different
3	19	Feels hopeless
4	41	Experiences usual sexual feelings
5	77	Has an increased interest in religion
6	104	Feels unable to make decisions
7	65	Concerned with "getting even" with others
8	2	Feels "at end of rope"
9	87	Expresses distrust of people in general—feels they will let him (her) down
10	45	Concern over waning sexual interest

Rank	*Least* Trait	
102	60	Can laugh at times
103	67	Feels optimistic
104	34	Professes to have little or no feelings
105	4	Gets much secondary gain from illness
106	37	Feels better now than previously
107	59	Feels as though things will get better in near future
108	13	Little sadness experienced
109	99	Feels hopeful about getting better
110	5	Feels he (she) brought illness on self
111	47	Anger is experienced

TABLE 12

THE 10 MOST AND 10 LEAST AGREED-ON STATEMENTS IN THE CURRENT BEHAVIOR LIST

Most Rank	*Trait*	
1	85	Generous with own possessions
2	60	Asks others to clarify questions and remarks
3	6	Asks many questions
4	86	More communicative with men than women
5	56	Changes topic of conversation frequently
6	72	Tries to lead others
7	80	Accepts gifts readily
8	8	Wants to learn about other people's lives and work
9	7	Avoids looking at others
10	5	Is interested in how others react to him (her)

Least Rank	*Trait*	
78	64	Languid and "overrelaxed"
79	74	Makes excessive demands on others
80	30	Denies need for help
81	12	Confides easily to others
82	43	Makes an effort to be cheerful even if feelings are different
83	29	Belittles own problems—describes them as transitory
84	1	Isolated and withdrawn
85	47	Apathetic
86	22	Overtly hostile
87	45	Expresses willingness to cooperate with others in mutual projects

TABLE 13

COMPOSITE PROFILE FOR 21 CASES ON
FEELINGS AND CONCERNS TRAIT SAMPLE*

Rank	Trait		Rank	Trait	Rank	Trait
1	19	Feels hopeless	22	21	45	5
2	18	Helpless and	23	2	46	49
		powerless	24	79	47	15
3	7	Feels a failure	25	101	48	50
4	16	Guilt feelings	26	25	49	90
5	12	Sadness and	27	64	50	54
		blueness	28	102	51	57
6	22	Loss of esteem	29	110	52	42
7	51	Feels lonely	30	1	53	76
8	14	Feels ashamed	31	108	54	38
9	104	Unable to make	32	83	55	62
		decisions	33	53	56	32
10	24	Feeling of	34	47	57	23
		tenseness	35	8	58	94
11	27		36	100	59	3
12	20		37	68	60	60
13	81		38	89	61	85
14	55		39	82	62	40
15	107		40	87	63	73
16	31		41	10	64	96
17	26		42	69	65	4
18	105		43	6	66	91
19	78		44	71	67	93
20	74					
21	33					

*The trait ranked 1 is the most characteristic of all patients; the trait ranked 111 is the most uncharacteristic of all patients.

(Continued)

TABLE 13 (Continued)

Rank	Trait	Rank	Trait	Rank	Trait	
68	44	83	34	98	43	
69	11	84	66	99	75	
70	97	85	29	100	37	
71	84	86	109	101	99	
72	92	87	95	102	56	Unable to cry
73	39	88	106	103	59	Optimistic
74	98	89	9	104	52	Closer to people
75	86	90	63	105	13	Little sadness
76	45	91	88	106	36	Feels excited
77	72	92	70	107	67	Optimistic
78	48	93	65	108	103	Quicker
79	110	94	46	109	30	Broad interests
80	61	95	77	110	28	Energetic
81	41	96	80	111	35	Elated
82	17	97	58			

TABLE 14

COMPOSITE PROFILE FOR 21 CASES ON THE
CURRENT BEHAVIOR TRAIT SAMPLE*

Rank	Trait		Rank	Trait
1	71	Cries or sobs	19	69
2	41	Recognizes need for help	20	50
			21	11
3	4	Other people source of help	22	ᵇ5
			23	26
4	19	Restless and fidgety	24	77
5	27	Clings to others	25	24
6	14	Relates in distant and guarded way	26	9
			27	21
7	1	Isolated and withdrawn	28	54
			29	57
8	35	Avoids strong emotions	30	52
9	59	Effort to be composed	31	44
			32	40
10	62	Impresses severity of problems	33	10
			34	49
11	13		35	7
12	5		36	79
13	15		37	80
14	39		38	75
15	74		39	38
16	33		40	87
17	28		41	86
18	61			

*The trait ranked 1 is the most characteristic of all patients; the trait ranked 87 is the most uncharacteristic of all patients.

(Continued)

TABLE 14 *(Continued)*

Rank	Trait		Rank	Trait	
42	43		66	3	
43	45		67	85	
44	83		68	63	
45	47		69	70	
46	81		70	17	
47	67		71	25	
48	32		72	53	
49	58		73	12	
50	23		74	78	
51	60		75	72	
52	46		76	68	
53	20		77	76	
54	82		78	34	Becomes less communicative
55	66				
56	31		79	84	Treats others as inferior
57	2		80	42	Ingratiating behavior
58	65		81	36	Speech mumbled
59	56		82	8	Curious about others
60	51		83	48	Eager to terminate conversation
61	18				
62	6		84	64	Languid and relaxed
63	16		85	30	Denies need for help
64	22		86	37	Accelerated speech
65	73		87	29	Belittles own problems

we tried to understand as clearly as possible what factors made for our unreliable ratings.

REASONS FOR THE DISCREPANCY

Having drawn on a background of experience with psychotherapy in which over a period of time many behavioral characteristics become apparent we had not realized that in restricted interviews oriented toward special goals we could not observe a great deal of action. Certainly this would be far less than observations of patients on nursing units for even a brief period. In other words, much of what we wanted to see was simply not displayed to us in the interview. Or it may be possible that the traits were vaguely worded and the observers could not attach them to behavior, but this would involve all raters equally and not necessarily disturb reliability.

Furthermore, an important reason that reliability was not affected by confused statements or difficulty in observations is that the relative amount of agreement on the list of "symptoms" (which will be discussed later) in the check list appears to parallel the relative amount of agreement in the current behavior sorts. That is, on those cases in which there is reasonably high reliability in the current behavior sorts, as shown by the alpha coefficients, there is fairly good agreement on the ratings of symptoms. When coefficient alpha is low, there seems to be less agreement on symptoms. As another piece of evidence, the three cases with the lowest alphas on the current behavior sample also have relatively low alphas on the feelings and concerns sample. It seems that we are confronted with lack of agreement that goes across different kinds of traits and across different kinds of rating tasks. The difficult is simply greater in the current behavior list than in the "feelings and concerns" list.

We know that psychiatrists are accustomed to working with affects and fantasies and become adept at understanding them and in communicating with fellow workers about them. They can attain a high degree of consistency in interpreting or inferring from

TABLE 15

COMPARISON OF THE CORRELATIONS BETWEEN
TWO PSYCHIATRISTS WHO SAW PATIENTS AND
TWO PSYCHIATRISTS WHO DID NOT SEE PATIENTS
(CURRENT BEHAVIOR TRAIT SAMPLE)

Case	"Saw"	"Did Not See"
1	.60	.47
2	.66	.41
3	.40	.30
4	.53	.10
5	.54	.42
6	.62	.34
9	.05	.49
12	.45	.41
13	.42	.39
17	.51	.52
19	.54	.34
Average	.48	.38
Average excluding case 9	.53	.37

patients' direct statements. However, they are not good observers of behavior, nor do they communicate behavioral information well to colleagues. If it were true that the difficulty was partly in communicating, then we might find differences in the correlations between those raters who actually saw the patient they were rating and those raters who had available only the written descriptions and heard the case presentations. This involves the assumption that the psychiatrists might have perceived behavioral traits, perhaps subliminally, but were not accustomed to thinking about or recording such information or conveying it accurately to others.

TABLE 16

AVERAGE CORRELATIONS OF EACH PSYCHIATRIST WITH
ALL OTHERS USING THE CURRENT BEHAVIOR TRAIT SAMPLE

Psychiatrist	Average Correlation
I	.37
II	.40
III	.37
IV	.46
V	.37
VI	.44
VII	.32

We had reasons to suspect that this might be correct and so proceeded with an analysis of differences between raters who had seen the patient and raters who had not. Because some of the cases had been seen by one of the psychiatrists who left the project before the ratings were done and so had to be excluded, and because a few were seen by only one peron, we analyzed only 11 cases. The average correlations of current behavior traits for psychiatrists who saw the patients were .48 as against .38 for those who did not see them, which is a significant difference (Table 15). If one case, which is an exception, is omitted, the correlations become .53 and .37 respectively.

The average correlation of each psychiatrist with all of the others on all cases on which he made ratings shows the tendency of the individual psychiatrist to agree with the other psychiatrists as a group (Table 16). This might be thought of as an index of communality of diagnosis. Psychiatrist IV is then the most typical and Psychiatrist VII is the least typical. However, the differences here even between the extremes are not large.

Thus it seemed that psychiatrists were not as adept at observing

TABLE 17

FACTOR LOADINGS FOR 20 CASES

Case	A	B	C	h^2
1	.54	.58	.00	.63
2	.83	.08	-.04	.68
3	.06	.60	-.06	.37
4	.76	-.01	-.10	.60
5	.85	-.06	.02	.73
6	.73	.28	-.16	.62
8	.65	.30	.35	.63
9	.65	.01	-.14	.43
10	.61	.55	-.02	.68
11	.67	.29	.26	.60
12	.78	.10	-.18	.64
13	.76	.06	-.12	.59
14	.80	.10	.24	.70
15	.79	.24	.32	.78
16	.76	.39	-.09	.74
17	.78	.00	.00	.61
18	.82	.16	.19	.73
19	.32	.67	.08	.56
20	.81	.28	.05	.73
21	.66	.38	-.40	.72

behavior as they were at eliciting feelings and concerns. Apparently in spite of specifically looking for behavioral traits, our interests and familiarity with content of thoughts and feelings interfere with our observation of what goes on in front of us. Paradoxically we can see and communicate better what we have to interpret and infer.

RESULTS OF THE ACTUAL FACTOR ANALYSIS
OF THE PILOT GROUP

All possible intercorrelations were computed among the composite profiles of 21 patients, each derived from combining the ratings of four psychiatrists. The matrix of intercorrelations was subjected to a centroid factor analysis. Six factors were extracted after which rotations were undertaken in order to obtain the most substantial and clear-cut factors possible. Three of the factors are prominent enough to warrant further investigation: A, B, and C (bipolar).

Correlation of the Data

The scores in Table 17 under columns A, B, and C refer to the patients' scores (correlation) on each of these factors. This correlation is between the person's composite sort (Table 13) which is his profile according to the Q-sort and the collection of traits that make up each factor. A loading score of .50 or over means that there is a substantial correlation between the patient's profile as determined by the Q-sort and the factor. A loading of .30 to .50 means a moderate correlation, and a score of .30 or less means that the factor and the patient do not correlate significantly. In other words, the size of the correlation indicates the extent to which the particular patient possesses traits which are similar to those comprising the particular factor.

In this same table, the column titled "h^2" represents the "communalities" of these patients. This indicates to what extent these three factors "explain" the profile as determined by the Q-sort. A high score of h^2 means that the patient's Q-sort could be accurately predicted from the three factors. A low score means that his sort could not accurately be predicted from the factors, and suggests the existence of other as yet undetermined factors. In this study communalities are generally high, meaning that the factors are potent explainers of our subjects.

Correlations among composite sorts in this study are generally substantial. They average about .50 and are numerous above .70. This shows two things. First, the composite sorts are reliable as our earlier results indicated they would be because unreliable measures cannot correlate highly with one another. Although it is not always a blessing to find high correlations among sorts, it does indicate high reliability. Second, although no strict comparison can be made, the correlations here are higher than those with adult and child neurotics and schizophrenics in other statistical studies. This indicates that "depressives" tend to be more alike than patients with other kinds of psychological abnormalities.

Factor Arrays

The factors are also presented as a rank order of traits and for practical purposes we designate only the top 20 traits in Factor A, the top 10 traits in Factor B, and the top and bottom 5 traits in Factor C. C being a bipolar factor characterizes patients by both the upper and lower end of the trait array. The statistical results support consideration of these groups of traits. Factor C and Negative C in this pilot group are statistically weak and small; future investigations will be necessary to verify their existence. Factors A and B are strong enough to stand at this point as definitive even in our small group of patients.

The factor arrays, A, B, C, and Negative C, are listed on the following pages.

Factor A

Rank Order	Trait	(In rank order 1-20)
1	19	Feels hopeless
2	12	Feelings are dominated by sadness and "blueness"
3	16	Guilt feelings experienced
4	18	Feels helpless and powerless
5	2	Feels "at end of rope"
6	74	Feels loss of interest in "oral satisfactions" —food, drink, and smoking
7	26	Has anxiety toward particular concerns
8	7	Feels a failure
9	31	Feels ambivalent toward important personal issues
10	55	Wants to cry much of the time
11	22	Feels loss of esteem by others
12	81	Feels that illness was precipitated by recent events
13	110	Preoccupation with physical symptoms
14	20	Feels self unworthy
15	14	Shame is experienced
16	51	Feels lonely
17	21	Feels unloved
18	78	Feels guilt for not assuming family and/or job responsibilities
19	5	Feels he (she) brought illness on self
20	33	Experiences moodiness

Factor B

Rank Order	Trait	(In rank order 1-10)
1	60	Can laugh at times
2	96	Concerned with material loss—money, property, etc.
3	18	Feels helpless and powerless
4	54	Feels burdened by demands of others
5	57	Feels envious of others

Factor B—Continued

Rank Order	Trait	
6	85	Feels that illness would be relieved by the solving of certain "material" problems—money, job, housing, etc.
7	25	Experiences free anxiety
8	27	Feels constantly fatigued
9	64	Feels "jittery"
10	11	Considers self as lazy

Factor C

Rank Order	Trait	(In rank order 1-5 positive pole)
1	6	Concerned with suffering caused others
2	76	Expresses much concern for the welfare of family and friends
3	93	Concerned with making up for wrongs to others
4	78	Feels guilt for not assuming family and/or job responsibilities
5	5	Feels he (she) brought illness on self

Factor C (Negative)

Rank Order	Trait	(In rank order 111-107 negative pole)
111	85	Feels that illness would be relieved by the solving of certain "material" problems—money, job, housing, etc.
110	4	Gets much secondary gain from illness
109	91	Concerned with aging and lessening vigor
108	96	Concerned with material loss—money, property, etc.
107	80	Feels that he (she) is being brave in bearing troubles.

Interpreting the Factors

It becomes immediately apparent that some of the items are duplicated in different factors. The three factors correlate almost exactly zero with one another. That is, there is over-all statistical independence among them. However, this does not prevent a few items appearing at the top of two or more factors. Whereas there may be several overlapping items in the high ends of two factors, there are also usually several that are at opposite ends. For example, "guilt feelings experienced" is high in both A and C. "Feels loss of interest in 'oral satisfactions'—etc." is high in A and on the negative end of C. In terms of interpreting the factors, it is the *pattern of traits* that counts. "Guilt feelings experienced" appears in different contexts in A and C and thus means different things.

At this point, as we stated in our prior discussion of factor analysis, we shall attempt to give meaning to each factor for subsequent testing and hypothesis-making. Using the traits composing each factor for this purpose, weaving them into a clinical picture and attaching interpretive meanings to the whole, is like assembling a whole model from an assortment of component parts and then trying to find out what the product is good for. We shall proceed to do this briefly with the factors of the pilot study and subsequently with all other factors found from our analyses.

Interpreting the factors in this manner we can hypothesize that Factor A describes a person who is internally pained and distressed, guilty, helpless, sad, regressed, and who has lost interest in the external world. This is the "garden variety," the stereotype or what may be called the typical depression. It is absent only in Patient 3 and low only in Patient 19.

Factor B describes someone who appears quite attached to the external world; so much so that he looks upon supplies from it as the answer to his illness. He too feels helpless but in a different way than the person in Factor A. His helplessness seems to reflect his inability to force the outside world to give to him, while the helplessness in Factor A seems closer to despair: a feeling that nothing from outside can matter and that he could not accept needed supplies even if they were offered to him. Males predominate in Factor B. The difference between male and female is statistically significant at the .02 level even with so few subjects. This question will be discussed later when other demographic variables such as age, sex, race, religion, and education are analyzed from our check list.

Factor C (positive pole) describes a person who is concerned about what he has done to others (presumably aggression) and about what restitutive efforts he can manage. Again this factor seems to describe a particular kind of person, or aspect of a person, which is differentiated from other characteristics described in other factors.

Factor C (negative pole) also describes concern with external loss, but in addition with internal loss possibly associated with aging. There is also the martyred feeling of being brave in bearing trouble. One could speculate that the concern with external loss is not identical with that in Factor B, but here represents a projection of a sense of inner change and loss of vigor.

Obviously other interpretations of the data can be made and we state these ideas only as tentative ways of looking at empirically derived factors. At this point they can do nothing but serve as a basis for further, more detailed and extensive, investigations. Nonetheless, the separation of these phenomena by empirical observation of depressed patients represents some distinction between people who share a "common" illness. It may serve as a basis, if confirmed, upon which to study varieties of depression from different points of view.

In an effort to make the various factors more vivid for the reader we present exemplifying case histories of patients falling predominantly in each factor.

CASE REPORTS

Case 1: Factor A

This patient is essentially a member of Factor A, characterized by the following traits: "feels hopeless, feelings dominated by sadness and 'blueness,' guilt feelings experienced, feels helpless and

powerless, feels 'at end of rope,' feels loss of interest in oral satisfaction (food, drink, and smoking), has anxiety toward particular
concerns, feels a failure, feels ambivalent toward important personal issues, wants to cry much of the time." The above are the
first ten and strongest traits in the factor and the next ten are
such traits as "feels loss of esteem by others, feels self unworthy,
shame is experienced, feels lonely, feels unloved." Preoccupation
with physical symptoms is also included in this list.

The patient is a fifty-four-year-old Jewish woman, admitted to
PPI following two recent admissions to the general hospital. Her
first admission was occasioned by a feeling that something behind
her sternum, probably a cancer, was choking her. An acute exacer-
bation of abdominal pain and anorexia continued following discharge from the hospital, in spite of an essentially negative medical
investigation.

The anorexia was of such proportions that a second hospitalization was necessary two months later because of malnutrition.
She was at that time fed intravenously. Since the first hospitalization
she had felt "sick" with insomnia, abdominal distension, constipation, fear of dying, hopelessness, and confusion in thinking. It
was noted that five days after her discharge from the general hospital she made a suicide attempt by ingesting sedatives and mercur-
ochrome. She explained that she had been preoccupied with
thoughts of killing herself in order to end her torture. At the time of
the PPI admission she was agitated, wringing her hands but unable
to cry. She was melancholic, complaining with a crying voice which
alternated with a calmer more normal voice. She expressed feelings
of hopelessness, seeing herself as dead and certain that she could
not get well. She had many suicidal fantasies and seemed perplexed
that at a time in her life when she had no responsibilities and should
be happy, she felt so miserable. Even though her material needs
were satisfied she could feel no comfort.

The present illness seemed to be precipitated by her son's departure for California and her daughter's plans for marriage. When

she learned that the daughter was not going to postpone her plans for marriage she made the suicide attempt. In addition to the despair and suffering the interviewer also noted that she would primp before his coming and made strong bids for his interest and attention. She was neatly dressed and at first glance appeared composed and quiet. Her movements and gait were slow. Facial expressions changed rapidly from composure to expressions of torment with moaning dry sobs. Sometimes a wide-eyed, staring expression was seen. Banging her head with her hands, assuming the fetal position on her bed, taking a stance as if she were standing on her head (her head on the table), staring out the window with her head in her hands pressed against the screen, all expressed her hopelessness and feeling that she could not get well. Hand-wringing was the most frequent expression of despair. She was curious to know if she was the worst patient that the interviewer had ever seen, explaining that she felt desperate whenever she realized that she had brought it all on herself. She elaborated by explaining that everything was gone, there was no hope, and that she was not getting well because she probably did not want to. She made the observation that it was too bad that the physical pain was gone for it was easier when she had *pain,* there was less *suffering.* She seemed clearly aware of the struggle within her between the desire to get well and the alternating feeling of wanting to die. She mentioned that she was ashamed of the way she looked.

Case 2: Factor B

This patient has many of the traits described in Factor B characterized by "can laugh at times, concerned with material loss (money, property, etc.), feels helpless and powerless, feels burdened by demands of others, feels envious of others, feels illness would be relieved by the solving of certain material problems (money, job, housing, etc.), experiences free anxiety, feels constantly fatigued, feels jittery, considers self as lazy." Other traits below these first ten include "feels hopeful about getting better, shame is experienced, feels failure, feels unable to make decisions, credits illness to excessive family and/or job responsibilities."

The patient was a fifty-seven-year-old Jewish male who had been a builder of speculative homes in a moderate-sized eastern town. He had been married for eighteen years. Originally raised in a lower-upper-class society he gradually sank to the middle-middle class. He dated the onset of his symptoms to some three months before admission, at which time he first noted nervousness and jitteriness. Prior to this he was carefree and not interested in money. About fifteen months before the onset of his illness he became seriously interested in a building project. He employed a young man as superintendent to whom he had promised a partner-ship if the venture were successful. On the contrary, it was a com-plete failure—a nightmare. People were continually on his neck complaining. The houses had serious drainage problems since they were built on the edge of a swamp and after heavy rainfalls the basements flooded. He was unable to sell four of the houses, still owed considerable money, and was dodging creditors. An older brother came to his rescue on the condition that the patient enter the hospital.

His symptoms consisted of depression, particularly in the early morning. He awakened at six o'clock and for the next three hours tried to force himself out of bed to get on the job. He knew that he was a failure, that he would certainly go bankrupt and lose every-thing, and that the only solution was to commit suicide. He felt that he could not face the problems of the day. The depression was deepest in the morning but as the day wore on he became easier in spirits and felt much better at nighttime. His wife bucked him up considerably and without her he felt worse and more lonely. With the depression he developed a severe envy which he never had before. He always depreciated people who spent money on pretentious material things but now he envied those who drove Cadillacs and traveled to Europe. In the morning he crawled into his wife's bed, holding her tightly and crying like a baby. He had been married, since shortly after the death of his mother, to a singer who had shown promise in show business. She constantly yearned to return to the bright lights and luxury of the big city. Prior to his marriage he had gone around for eight years with a Catholic girl and lived with her but didn't marry her on account of his family, to whom he was financially bound. He and his wife wrangled throughout their marriage. He was often pompous, irritable, and erratic, and frequently shouted violently at his daughter.

His family started in the junk business, and were now in scrap iron. All of the brothers and sisters fared much better financially than the patient. He never wanted to go into the business, had no interest in providing for himself, and lived on the income from some inherited property and stocks. His older brother, who did stay in the business, was a millionaire at twenty-nine.

Throughout his married life he had shown little regard for his wife and only child. He insisted on his own way in the most infantile manner. In the occasion of a previous discharge from a hospital his wife had brought him the wrong shirt. He screamed at her and insisted that she go home and get a different shirt just for him to wear going home from the hospital. When he was told he should take it easy because of high blood pressure he didn't do a bit of work for two years. He stayed home all the time, interfered with his wife's housework and shopping, and made many critical remarks. His wife left him on a number of occasions, only to return at his pleading and insistence. At the time of his breakdown, which developed suddenly, he began to blame himself, crying and telling his wife that she was right all the time and that he had neglected his work. He then began to torture himself, blaming himself for everything including the rain that flooded the property. He remembered the details of all the things he had done wrong and criticized himself because others had gambled during the housing boom and had become rich.

His own financial records were in terrible condition and he knew that he never should have been in business. He paid no attention to income tax returns, simply letting someone fill them out for him. He kept no accurate figures nor did he make accurate appraisals of the cost of the housing project. In talking of the project he told of his brother's offer to take over, which gave him great relief. It did not seem to be enough to cure him. He wondered if his brother would stop helping him when he found out the extent of his need for money. As long as he was sick he couldn't do anything. If he got better he would still need financial help.

It seemed that the death of his parents, the economic recession, rejection by the brother, and the demands of his wife forced this patient, who up to the age of forty had gotten by with doing no work and living as a helpless dependent child, into responsibility. There was always considerable anxiety about it, but he showed a semblance of activity with a pseudo-masculine aggressiveness in the family situation. Underlying this, however, was a very strong regressive pull, and whatever equilibrium he achieved was broken down by the disappointment of the housing project. He was considerably overweight, nibbling all the time. Attempts at reduction of weight consisted only of taking medication. He fantasied that his illness would bring him back into the family circle and that then his brother would help him. He was dependent and an aggressively demanding person with a pretense of masculine activity in sex and business, believing somehow or other that God or father would provide. The recent disappointment resulted in regression with frank demands, some shame, a considerable oral envy, and depression.

Case 3: Positive Factor C

This patient shows many traits found in Positive Factor C, composed of the following traits: "concern with suffering caused others, expresses much concern for the welfare of family and friends, concern with making up for wrongs to others, feels guilt for not assuming family and/or job responsibilities, feels he brought illness on self, wants to cry much of the time, increased sexual feelings and interest, guilt feelings experienced, concern over increasing sexual interest, professes to have little or no feelings." In our study Factor C was quite small, with only two patients showing significant scores. Thus some of the elements in C are harder to see in the total clinical picture. Many of the characteristics of this factor are shared with Factor A. However, the differentiation seems to be on the basis of much greater guilt over suffering caused to other people. The appearance of increasing sexual interest may be artifact, but also may have to do with attempts to project guilt feelings onto sexuality rather than recognize other more unacceptable impulses.

The patient was a forty-year-old Jewish woman, married to a physician, the mother of two daughters. She was admitted to PPI for a recurrent depression, having had several prior hospitalizations. Her first depression had occurred eleven years before admission and six years prior to admission she began working in psychotherapy. Although the over-all course was a gradual and slow improvement it was interrupted by repeated episodes of depression, some with suicidal ideas, and more or less genuine suicide attempts occurring at two-year intervals.

The most recent depression appeared to be precipitated by a combination of several circumstances. Some six months earlier the patient moved into a new apartment which was the nicest and most luxurious place in which the family had ever lived. This seemed to be an experience to which she was specifically vulnerable since after a previous move she had also become depressed. Her therapist felt that there was intense guilt over her wish to take from others, and for her to be in luxury served only to augment the guilt and precipitate a clinical depression. Her husband did not notice much depression after the move, but her therapist felt that he saw clear indications of it. More recently she gave a party celebrating the Bar Mitzvah of her sister's children and most recently a party for own daughter's confirmation. It seemed that when the children became the center of attention her own envy was mobilized and revived memories of her own deprivations, guilt, and consequent clinical illness developed.

About a month prior to her admission she became aware of feeling sad, discouraged, listless, and easily fatigued. She felt she could not cope with the family responsibilities and was overwhelmed by the things that she had to do. Characteristically, in the midst of her depression one of her main complaints was that she didn't feel anything. It is almost as if she had no relations with other people. She heard what they said and understood their meanings, but did not have her usual feeling responses. She spoke mainly about the suffering imposed on her daughter by her illness. She repeatedly criticized herself for her inadequacy, felt that it was a failure to require hospitalization again, especially since it separated her from the daughter. She awakened between five and six in the morning and then experienced her most intense depression. During her depression she had difficulty in eating because of tensely drawn facial muscles which became quite painful.

Case 4: Positive Factor C

This is another example of a patient showing the traits of Positive Factor C. The patient was a thirty-four-year-old married Jewish woman. She appeared listless and guarded at first, rapidly becoming more demanding and insistent in her request for help. There was much apathy and hopelessness and she felt that she could only get well if treated in some magical way by drugs or somatic treatment. She repeated many self-recriminations, feeling that in some way she was directly responsible for all that happened to her and that she should leave the hospital and take care of her children. She frequently expressed the feeling that she should be very ashamed about the neighbors' finding out about her illness and that they would reject her children because of it. She expressed her concern about what this could do to the children.

The onset of illness was dated to shortly after her return from a one-week automobile trip to the East Coast. She had recently learned to drive and had decided during the summer to become more outgoing and aggressive and more acceptable to people in general. She had never done anything like taking an automobile trip and this became quite important to her. It seemed that learning to drive and taking the trip were important steps in asserting her independence and self-sufficiency as a compensation for no longer being needed at home. Her husband had become more and more successful in business, and this resulted in his spending more time away from home and having less need for her. Her twelve-year-old son was maturing physically and becoming more independent of her, something about which she felt great anxiety and confusion. Her husband was opposed to her trip, could not accompany her because of business pressure, and felt that she was not a good enough driver to attempt it. She insisted on going anyway with her mother and brother and she and her husband parted on bad terms.

On her return she discovered that her husband's brother and a friend of the brother's had moved into the house and they were planning to stay for an indefinite period of time. She was unhappy about this and discussed it with her husband, but he would do nothing. She felt resentful but also powerless to do anything about the situation and tried to run the household with the added people. She found herself more and more overwhelmed by the demands and also by the stimulation. She reports profound confusion in trying to separate the underwear of the men when doing the laundry. She became progressively more confused and frightened; tried to appeal to neighbors for help and made increasing demands on her husband. Recognizing that she was unable to cope with the house and that her further presence there was detrimental to the children, she herself requested hospitalization.

In this study it was not possible to obtain enough understanding of the patient's background and character structure to evaluate the meaning of her symptoms fully and to understand her particular reaction in relation to the precipitating circumstances. It did seem clear, however, that she demonstrated two of the important aspects which this factor differentiates: namely, concern and guilt over what she was doing to other people and also rising concern over sexual impulses which in this case seemed to have been stirred by the additional men in the house and perhaps also by her son's pubescence.

Case 5: Negative Factor C

This is an example revealing the following traits of Negative Factor C: "feels that illness would be relieved by the solving of certain material problems—money, job, housing, etc.; gets much secondary gain from illness; concern with aging and lessening vigor; concern with material loss—money, property, etc.; feels that he is being brave in bearing troubles.

The patient was a fifty-eight-year-old, unemployed Jewish man who had been a carnival weight-guesser. The patient entered the hospital because of a progressive sense of hopelessness, somatic symptoms, suicidal ideas, and inability to work. He had been a chronic drifter for most of his adult life, working in the carnival business since his late teens. Until 1945 or 1946 he and his wife had a weight-guessing and jewelry concession with a traveling carnival or, more correctly, a succession of traveling carnivals, but went bankrupt. Since that time until some twenty months prior to admission he had worked at odd jobs, usually as a messenger for jewelry concerns. He presented himself as a well-traveled cosmopolitan "man of the world," someone who had really lived and who knew what life was all about. This feeling of importance and worldliness seemed to have been an essential part of his psychic economy and even in more recent days, when he worked as a messenger, he gained a great feeling of importance from carrying valuable jewels from place to place.

He recognized that he was a difficult person to get along with and that he always had trouble with bosses, but felt that if he only had money for a stake he could go back to the carnival business and everything would be all right. He was bitter about having no one to give or lend him money, and since he himself had been unable to work for the last twenty months he had been entirely dependent upon his wife's earnings from her job as a bookkeeper. He protested that he should have some shame and guilt about letting his wife take care of him, but he actually seemed to experience very little of this. In recent months she had been more insistent on his getting a job and the final precipitant leading to psychiatric consultation was her giving him a list of want ads and telling him that he should look into them He got up, had breakfast, and, just as he was preparing to go out, had a "blackout," fell, and could not leave the house. His wife knew that this happened each time he was to look for a job, but nonetheless permitted him to stay home. He was concerned with his getting older and part of his difficulty in finding a job he blamed on his age.

Although this seemed to have been an insidious and progressively developing depression, there had been some recent accentuating stresses too. His son noted a change in his father at the time of his graduation from high school. This actually antedated by several months the patient's own statement of the onset of his illness, but the son noted that the father seemed less confident, less interested, and more withdrawn after his graduation. The son entered the army and while in the service married a girl against his parents' wishes. The parents, who were both Jewish, described this girl as an "Arkansas hillbilly" and tried to get the son to annul his marriage. He was tempted but finally resisted and furthermore told his parents that when he was discharged he was going to live in the South. His father had long had the fantasy that his son would return and that together they would go into business, probably some carnival enterprise. Although he was vague and it was difficult to pin down precisely what his feelings were, the impression during the interview was that in fantasy the father would be the strong one helping the son to set up a business by virtue of his greater wisdom and experience. In reality, the son would run the business and take care of the father. So it seems here that the patient was concerned with the real loss of someone to care for him, in addition to being reminded of his own advancing age by his son's maturation. It seems as though the inner awareness of his own waning abilities left him with no resources with which to maintain his self-esteem.

SUMMARY

Psychiatrists' ratings of the feelings and concerns check list were highly reliable and could be utilized in factor-analytic studies. On the other hand, their ratings of "current behavior" did not show correlation coefficients of sufficiently high reliability (agreement) to warrant factor analysis. The rank order of agreement for both trait lists and the composite profiles derived from them give a fairly adequate clinical picture of the over-all depressive syndrome. Efforts to understand the reasons for low reliability among the investigators' ratings of current behavior led us to conclude that psychiatrists were not as adept at observing behavior as they are at inferring and interpreting feelings and concerns. Paradoxically, they "see" and communicate better about feelings than behavior.

Factor-analytic studies of feelings and concerns disclosed two strong factors (A and B) and one weak factor (C). The rank order of significant traits composing each factor can be interpreted in terms of types of depressed patients, making good sense in relation to clinical experience as illustrated by exemplifying case reports.

The statistical confirmation that several psychiatrists can examine a group of patients and report significant differences sufficiently sharp to separate subgroups was to us an exciting and challenging finding. Although the temptation was great to interpret these groups in "dynamic" terms and to speculate about origins and processes, we tried to minimize this so as not to interfere with the larger study which was projected and which seemed clearly worthwhile.

~~~~~~~~~~~~~~~~~~~~~~~~~~~~~~~~

CHAPTER 5

Stereotypes and Check Lists

BEFORE DISCUSSING THE RESULTS OF OUR ANALYSES
of the remaining check list, we first present a control study which
attempts to guard against the biases and preconceptions of the
raters. What do they have in mind as the typical clinical manifestations of depression? If we knew the "stereotype of depression"
maintained by the researchers, we could have some idea of the
degree to which they were seeing, inferring, and recording accurate observations about the subjects, and how much they were
projecting their own image of what a depressed patient ought to
feel and how he should behave. This should be valuable as a further assessment of the reliability of our ratings and serve as a
base line from which to judge further conclusions.

DETERMINING THE STEREOTYPES OF DEPRESSION
HELD BY THE RATERS

Each member of the group, therefore, sorted the Q-cards for
his own personal idea of what a depressed patient was like. First we
present the study on feelings and concerns stereotypes. Intercorrelations were obtained among the seven sorts, the three factors which
were previously reported in the feelings and concerns analysis, and

TABLE 18

INTERCORRELATIONS* OF PSYCHIATRIC SORTS FOR
FEELINGS AND CONCERNS STEREOTYPE

	F_a	F_b	F_c	Total Composite	Psychiatrist						
					I	II	III	IV	V	VI	VII
F_a	--	-07	03	90	76	63	80	76	58	73	67
F_b	-07	--	-01	31	02	00	08	05	07	22	13
F_c	03	-01	--	01	03	-11	04	13	04	-01	06
Total Composite	90	31	01	--	74	61	80	76	58	82	71
Psychiatrist											
I	76	02	03	74	--	55	73	73	51	64	56
II	63	00	-11	61	55	--	68	69	60	68	64
III	80	08	04	80	73	68	--	79	68	77	69
IV	76	05	13	76	73	69	79	--	65	76	70
V	58	07	04	58	51	60	68	65	--	62	60
VI	73	22	-01	82	64	68	77	76	62	--	74
VII	67	13	06	71	56	64	69	70	60	74	--

*Decimal points omitted. Thus, 50 should be understood as .50.

a total composite of the average sorts for the 21 cases (Table 18).
In addition to the specific relationships, the essential findings from
the feelings and concerns stereotype are as shown in Table 18.

Feelings and Concerns

There is a well-agreed-upon stereotype of the depressed patient's
feelings and concerns. The lowest correlation is .51. However, most
of the correlations are in the .60's and .70's, and three correlations
are above .75. The psychiatric stereotypes are very much like the

TABLE 19

INTERCORRELATIONS* OF PSYCHIATRIC SORTS FOR
CURRENT BEHAVIOR STEREOTYPE

	Total Composite	Psychiatrist						
		I	II	III	IV	V	VI	VII
Total Composite	--	63	47	55	67	50	57	40
Psychiatrist								
I	63	--	26	59	55	47	39	42
II	47	26	--	46	11	46	67	55
III	55	59	46	--	52	31	53	50
IV	67	55	11	52	--	34	28	15
V	50	47	46	31	34	--	56	54
VI	57	39	67	53	28	56	--	61
VII	40	42	55	50	15	54	61	--

*Decimal points omitted

total composite trait pattern. Here either the stereotype was confirmed, or the raters forced the stereotype on the 21 cases.

On relating the stereotypes to the three factors A, B, and C described in the previous chapter, the psychiatric sorts are highly related to Factor A and Factor A only. The total composite correlates .90 with Factor A. In no case does a stereotype sort correlate to any significant extent with either Factor B or C. In fact, the highest correlation was .22, achieved by Psychiatrist VI with Factor B. There are no apparent subdivisions among the psychiatrists regarding the feelings and concerns stereotype. The correlations are too high and too homogeneous to suggest that more than one factor plays a prominent role in the ratings.

The correlations among the sorts for the stereotype are considerably higher on the average than the correlations among sorts for individual patients, as outlined previously. Consequently the unreliability in the sorts for particular patients cannot be due to lack of consensus on the "typical depression." If psychiatrists had rated only in terms of the stereotype instead of rating the particular patients under study, correlations would have been much higher. Also, since Factors B and C were ascribed to numerous patients, psychiatrists are able to see beyond their stereotype (almost identical with Factor A) to look at particular trait patterns in individual cases.

Current Behavior

The analysis of the current behavior stereotype, however, showed quite different results and partially explains the difficulty in correlations of this trait list. Correlations among current behavior ratings are considerably lower on the average than among the feelings and concerns ratings. Some of the low correlations are .11, .15, .26, .31, .34. There is obviously much less agreement about the current behavior stereotype (Table 19).

Correlations with the total composite are substantial, but considerably less than those shown in the feelings and concerns sorts. In his studies on schizophrenia, Beck (1956) reported the same finding using two psychiatrists and two psychologists.

FACTORS ELICITED

The correlations are sufficiently heterogeneous to suggest that there is more than one factor operating. Upon subsequent factor analysis this proved to be the case. Two factors (called here Alpha and Beta) exist within the research groups' stereotypes of current behavior. Four raters have only Factor Alpha; one has a mixture of Alpha and Beta with Beta slightly predominating; one has a mixture which is mostly Beta; and one is almost all Beta (Table 20). The Alpha group corresponding to Factor A is the isolated withdrawn depression, while the Beta group is similar to Factor B,

TABLE 20

LOADINGS ON CURRENT BEHAVIOR
STEREOTYPE FACTORS

Psychiatrist	Factor	
	Alpha	Beta
I	.82	.00
II	.86	.03
III	.78	.05
IV	.81	-.11
V	.54	.64
VI	.47	.71
VII	.26	.80

the more talkative, demanding, clinging depression. Mixtures of these in the stereotype suggest the possibility of a composite of alternating phases or the use of a longer time dimension—in other words, *the stereotype of a patient improving over time.*

This relative lack of agreement among psychiatrists may account for some of the unreliability in the ratings of particular patients. It would seem, since there is more agreement when the psychiatrists actually saw the patient, that when data are lacking there is a tendency to fall back on the stereotype to fill in the blank spaces. Since there is disagreement about the stereotype, when it is relied upon to decide upon the position of some traits, the resulting correlations are also lower.

The factor arrays for the sterotypes are:

Factor Alpha		Highest Traits
Rank	Trait	
1	1	Isolated and withdrawn
2	71	Cries and sobs in presence of others
3	32	Reluctant to talk
4	54	Engrossment in own feelings lowers awareness of the presence of others

Factor	Alpha	Highest Traits—Continued
Rank	Trait	
5	47	Apathetic
6	20	Inattentive and distracted
7	27	Clings to others
8	18	Careless and unbecoming posture
9	63	Talks only when spoken to
10	14	Relates in a distant and guarded manner

Lowest Traits

87	38	Alert and responsive
86	8	Wants to learn about other people's lives and work
85	31	Considerable pressure to talk
84	29	Belittles own problems—describes them as transitory
83	30	Denies need for help
82	37	Speech is accelerated
81	72	Tries to lead others
80	11	Friendly
79	76	Tries to calm and reassure others
78	34	Becomes less communicative as relationships develop

Factor	Beta	Highest Traits
Rank	Trait	
1	31	Considerable pressure to talk
2	4	Regards other people as a source of help
3	27	Clings to others
4	26	Wants other people to evaluate his (her) condition
5	77	Acts as though others are obligated to help him (her)
6	8	Wants to learn about other people's lives and work
7	83	Makes an effort to agree with others
8	74	Makes excessive demands on others
9	62	Tries to impress others with severity of own problems
10	13	Is relieved to be able to talk with someone

Factor	Beta	Lowest Traits
Rank	Trait	
87	32	Reluctant to talk
86	63	Talks only when spoken to
85	64	Languid and "overrelaxed"
84	29	Belittles own problems—describes them as transitory
83	48	Eager to terminate conversations
82	18	Careless and unbecoming posture
81	87	Switches activities frequently
80	37	Speech is accelerated
79	2	Tries to impress others with own talents
78	30	Denies need for help

SIGNIFICANCE OF THE STEREOTYPICAL FACTORS

One comparison between our factors and the groups of patients who demonstrated high "loadings" in each of them was obvious and immediate. The patients who showed heavy loadings on Factor A were all women, while the high-loadings patients on Factor B were all men. In fact, many of us when discussing depressions in general automatically refer to the patient as "she," indicating the sex of our stereotypes. We considered this question of sex-linkage and speculated about its meaning. Factor B, which is concerned with external supplies and losses, in terms of material things, might be a characteristic way of responding for the male, whose primary orientation is toward work and providing for his family. To determine whether this was a dynamic difference, a different ego response to a similar dynamic process, a more general sex-linked characteristic related to other differences between depression in men and women, or only a statistical or sampling artifact, required further investigation with a larger sample.

TABLE 21

FREQUENCY OF SYMPTOMS

Frequency	*Trait No.*	*Symptom*
14	(2)	Decreased appetite
12	(3)	Difficulty in getting to sleep
10	(4)	Wakeful during night
9	(33)	Diminished appetite
8	(5)	Constipation (since illness)
8	(32)	Requires sedation to sleep
8	(50)	Thought processes slowed
6	(10)	Dryness of mouth
6	(16)	Weight loss
5	(18)	Preoccupation with physical symptoms which have no organic basis
5	(20)	Experiences tension as a somatic symptom referred to specific organ or area
5	(49)	Confusion
5	(55)	Impaired concentration

Other Traits

SYMPTOMS

We turn now to our check list of symptoms, which were rated by four psychiatrists on 21 patients. In the analysis no consideration was given to the judged importance of a trait. Instead, a simple frequency count was made of the number of times each trait was checked (Table 21). In other words, we were concerned with whether a trait like "increased appetite" was marked at all rather than with the degree indicated by the 1, 2, or 3 scale. The first step was to determine the traits which were agreed on for each patient. The decision was to record a trait as characteristic of the patient if three of the four psychiatrists checked it. This pro-

TABLE 22

STEREOTYPE OF SYMPTOMS BY FOUR PSYCHIATRISTS FOR
TYPICAL DEPRESSION

Agreed on by All Four Psychiatrists

Symptom

2. Decreased appetite
3. Difficulty in getting to sleep
16. Weight loss
32. Requires sedation to sleep
33. Diminished appetite
50. Thought processes slowed
59. Diminished ability to communicate

Agreed on by Three out of Four Psychiatrists

Symptom

4. Wakeful during night
5. Constipation (since illness)
10. Dryness of mouth
38. Wrings hands
49. Confusion
55. Impaired concentration

Agreed on by Two out of Four Psychiatrists

Symptom

8. Headaches (since illness)
11. Bad taste in mouth
12. Change in hair texture and dryness
14. Dryness of skin
18. Preoccupation with physical symptoms which have no organic basis
19. Delusions about body function
20. Experiences tension as a somatic symptom referred to specific organ or area
22. Unrealistic fear of cancer
25. Belching
39. Strikes self with hands
42. Picks at self or clothing
45. Suspicious of others
48. Disorganized thinking
52. Thought processes circumstantial
56. Blocking in train of thought
57. Attention impaired

vided a composite profile for each patient, consisting entirely of
1's and 0's. Frequency counts (166) were then made for each trait.

In Table 22 the stereotypes of symptoms agreed upon by 4, 3,
and 2 psychiatrists are listed. It is interesting that the stereotype
consensus resembles a *retarded depression,* that of 3 out of 4
psychiatrists an *agitated depression,* and that of 2 out of 4 includes
many *psychosomatic symptoms* and profound cognitive disturbances.

DREAMS

The frequency of dreams was very low. For half the patients a
zero rating was given and only four were marked more than once.
The actual frequency is given in Table 23. The failure to find
larger frequencies of agreed-on dreams could be due to several
things. First, it might be that psychiatrists check numerous dreams
but do not agree with one another about the dream characteristics
of particular patients. Second, it might be that the patients have
few dreams. Third, it might be that psychiatrists have little opportunity to obtain information about dreams during diagnostic
interviews with depressed patients. The third possibility seems the
most reasonable, for the over-all frequency is very small. It seems
doubtful, under our system of obtaining information about patients,
that the dream list could result in significant findings.

PREMORBID PERSONALITIES AND PSYCHODYNAMICS

We spent considerable time discussing the records of the interviews made by the psychiatrists on 21 patients. In our original
plan we hoped to delineate the premorbid personalities of our subjects and to formulate the psychodynamics of the depressive illness.
We were unable to achieve either of these goals.

Very little accurate information was available about our patients'
early lives. In the depressive mood they were unable to give us
much data. Since most of them were in middle life there were few
available informants who knew much about the patients' develop-

TABLE 23

FREQUENCY OF DREAMS

Frequency	Trait No.	Dream Characteristic
3	(1)	Has frightening dreams
2	(12)	Dreams which involve solving a problem which is never solved
2	(15)	Dreams contain people
2	(21)	Dreams of being in a moving vehicle

mental history. Information regarding the premorbid personality was bare of details except for generally stated descriptions indicating compulsivity, fluctuating moods, dependency, masochism, etc. Thus we abandoned our attempt to document genetic history and premorbid personality structure.

We also found that we could not successfully formulate the dynamics of the patients' illnesses, often failing to agree with each other as to what was important, and, at other times, while agreeing about formulations, being unable to document them to our own satisfaction. The more carefully we studied these patients, the more complex the problem appeared. To formulate the psychodynamics from the information obtained in a few interviews would have required a mutilating choice of data according to bias or stereotype. It is difficult enough and often impossible to accomplish in psychotherapeutic or even in psychoanalytic settings. Yet this circus feat is attempted at clinical conferences in most psychiatric training centers and hospitals. We could not blithely pursue such a course in our research because of the restraining influence of several keen investigators.

PRECIPITATING EXPERIENCES

However, we analyzed the check lists concerned with precipitating experiences and their meanings to the patient. We had to

TABLE 24

FREQUENCY OF PRECIPITATING EVENTS

Frequency	Trait No.	Precipitating Experience
8	(1)	Death (other than suicide)
6	(19)	Change in work role
6	(22)	Separation from family
4	(44)	Financial insecurity

ignore the "person who experienced event" and record only whether the event occurred or not. That is, we made no distinction between death of the mother and death of the father. To have obtained frequencies for all persons as well as all events would have resulted in 975 frequency counts, which would have probably taken much more time than the present analysis merits. We know now that had we made all of the possible frequency counts the vast majority would have been zero, and it is doubtful that any frequency would have been larger than 2 or 3. The most frequently agreed-on precipitating experiences are given in Table 24.

Whereas lack of information probably accounts for the sparsity of frequently-occurring dream characteristics, we doubt that is the case with precipitating experiences. Probably the more important reason for the low frequencies in the precipitating experiences list is the great particularity of the events. However, in addition to analysis of the precipitating experiences check list we studied the complete reports of each patient carefully and attempted in group meetings to arrive at some consensus. Most frequently multiple experiences seemed to be involved, converging over variable time spans and ultimately exceeding the patients' adaptive and integrative capacities. We speculated about whether any one of them if taken by itself would have been profound enough to precipitate a depression. We could frequently arrive at two or more possibilities but it was quite clear that to differentiate between these, or to exclude others, required far more data than could be elicited by a diagnostic study. A few clinical examples will serve to illustrate these points.

CASE REPORTS

Case 6

A thirty-six-year-old white male was admitted to the hospital with concern over inadequacy at his job, feeling that he could not continue, and with some suicidal ideas. It was difficult to determine the onset of the depressive reaction but it appeared to have become noticeable some six months before admission. There was evidence, however, that its onset, or at least some of the experiences related to its onset, dated to more than two years prior to his admission.

The patient had been employed as an assistant buyer by a mail order firm. Some two years prior to his admission his supervisor died. This was a man to whom he had been quite close and while working for him he had taken over much of the responsibility for running the department. He felt that he would have liked this man's job when he died, but was not too surprised when a successor was brought in from outside. In subsequent interviews with him some regret and disappointment about this were expressed. However, he continued to feel pretty well, although he occasionally had some concern over whether he might have contributed to the death of his superior by not making things easier for him. Some nine months prior to admission he was promoted to the position of buyer. Following this there was a steady downhill course with greater and greater preoccupation with inadequacy, anxiety and difficulty in sleeping and eating, weight loss, feelings of worthlessness, suicidal preoccupation, and minor somatic symptoms. A few weeks before admission these feelings became acute and he thought seriously about killing himself with a rifle, which precipitated his entry into the hospital.

In the third interview the patient told us more details about his promotion. He had formerly been working as assistant buyer in men's underwear, an item which sold steadily throughout the year. If he estimated his purchases incorrectly it was not critical. If he bought too much he simply cut down subsequent buying; if he bought too little he could reorder at any time. His promotion to buyer also involved a transfer to another department in which he had no previous experience. He was made buyer for men's wallets and leather goods, a highly seasonal item with 85 per cent of the sales taking place from the Christmas catalog. This meant that he was exposed now to a totally different situation in his work. In April he would have to set up the Christmas catalog and do his buying. If he overbought they were simply left with the merchandise which could not be sold; if he underbought they would not have sufficient merchandise to fill their Christmas orders, would lose business and alienate customers.

It was at this time that he began to show manifest signs of illness. At first glance this sounds like a man with guilt over his aggressive and competitive impulses who, upon obtaining promotion, could not tolerate the unconscious guilt over what the promotion meant. In this context one could formulate the activation of an old conflict and make very good sense out of his illness, which occurred against a background of the death of his superior and might have reactivated infantile aggressive fantasies. However, with more detail it became clear that in addition to the promotion he also found himself confronted with a totally new responsibility for which he considered himself quite unprepared. Obviously these two phenomena are not unrelated, and yet one finds it difficult to assign responsibility for the depression to a single dynamic operation. One could raise the question of whether, if this man had been promoted to buyer in the department he knew, or had been transferred to the seasonal department but not given full responsibility, the clinical illness would have developed. On the basis of the data we could cite the predominant exigencies related to the illness but could not make a further differentiation nor clarify the specific psychodynamic details.

A thirty-four-year-old white single woman, working as a psychologist and personal director in Chicago, lacked only her thesis for a doctorate in psychology. Her predominant complaints on admission were fatigue, feelings of being at the end of her rope, a sense of hopelessness, and a feeling that she could no longer go on and could no longer take care of herself amidst the problems and strains to which she had been exposed.

She dated the onset of her difficulty to some twenty months prior to her admission. She had been holding a highly responsible position and frequently worked up to eighty hours a week, partly because of the demands of the job and partly because of an inner drive to work long and arduous hours. Twenty months prior to admission she had gone out of town on a speaking engagement, something she had done frequently. She felt especially fatigued at this time although she was not quite clear about why. Cabs were difficult to get at the airport when she returned to the city and she shared a taxi with a strange man. During the ride he became more and more friendly and although she recognized this as a "line" she felt it was a pleasant diversion and became more interested in him. Had she been less fatigued and exhausted she would probably have paid no attention to him. On arrival downtown he invited her for a drink and he subsequently took her home. She invited him up to her apartment and said that what followed amounted to "rape." Later she modified this to assault rather than rape and in retrospect she recognized the incongruity of a thirty-four-year-old woman inviting a man to her apartment under these circumstances and not expecting any sexual activity. Following the incident, however, she felt disgusted, angry, and guilty and had no further desire to see him again. Shortly thereafter she began to feel fatigued and weak, and consulted a physician who diagnosed infectious mononucleosis and pregnancy. She was dazed, frightened, and depressed, and arranged for an abortion which afterwards left her with feelings of even greater guilt. This was the first time she had done anything illegal or dishonest.

After the abortion she went home to a small midwestern town for the Christmas holidays and found as usual that her family turned to her for advice about their problems. She returned to Chicago after the holidays and on arrival surprised a burglar in her apartment. This time she was really raped at knife point. She called the police but felt embarrassed and ashamed about it and also concerned about whether any information about her abortion would come out. She feared that she would conceive from the second rape and although her doctor said this was improbable she subsequently found that she was pregnant and had a second abortion.

Things remained relatively stable until the spring of that year, at which time she went to a convention with her boss. She kept their relations on a strictly business basis although she had the impression that he would have liked it otherwise. While there she met a friend of his whom she describes in much the same way as she describes her boss, and began to develop an intense romantic relationship with him. This lasted for a year, after which he became engaged to a girl in his home town. She was intensely disappointed at this news, which was the final precipitant that led her to seek psychiatric care. The details of this last relationship are not at all clear but it seems that it contained a large element of fantasy.

In response to attempts to explore this she becomes mildly angry and annoyed. Throughout our diagnostic work-up there were hints of involved fantasies about her own boss and indications that the relationship with the man from out of town was a displacement of feelings oriented toward him.

To recapitulate the events described as relating to the development of the illness, they include (a) a background of intense work, of little gratification and prolonged physical fatigue, (2) the initial sexual experience with pregnancy, the development of infectious mononucleosis, the added fatigue, the abortion, the return to Chicago, the rape and second pregnancy, the second abortion, the trip with her employer, the relationship with the boss's friend, the disappointment in this relationship followed by the development of more acute symptoms.

This patient's life even before these recent events is depicted as one huge masochistic crisis after another. Again, as with the previous patient, it becomes difficult to isolate a single or several meaningful precipitating experiences from the others, or to understand the dynamic details involved. It was clear that many of the experiences were unconsciously provoked by the patient, but even though self-induced the stresses exceeded her tolerance for punishment. For a masochistically oriented woman it is difficult to see why repeated disappointments of this nature should produce a clinical depression. The possibility remains that at some level of awareness she had some impending sense of pleasure at gratification or fulfillment of an unconscious wish. Instead of the illness being precipitated by all the deprivation and stress, it may be a response to the threatened fulfillment of the hidden and forbidden wish. In this context the allusions to feelings about her employer suggests the nature of these wishes. This is highly speculative and probably could not be clarified without intensive psychotherapeutic or psychoanalytic work. There is clearly great difficulty in precisely defining the precipitants or the dynamics of the depression.

Case 8

A thirty-six-year-old white housewife with a high-school education and belonging to the lower middle class was admitted to the hospital with complaints of loneliness; sadness; feelings of hopelessness, helplessness, and worthlessness; suicidal ideas; fatigue; and anxiety. Although self-depreciatory ideas and feelings of inadequacy appear to have been present for many years, she and her husband date the onset of the current illness to approximately a year prior to admission. At that time she consulted a gynecologist for some rather nonspecific complaints including difficulty in having sexual relations with her husband and was told, "I don't see how you can have a normal sex life." She stated that she was given no more specific information about what was wrong with her and no therapeutic recommendation was made. She did retain, however, the strong conviction that there was something wrong with her as a woman.

She was born and raised in a small town in the South, had met her husband while he was stationed there in the army, and had come to Chicago with him some ten years ago. She had never felt comfortable in the big city and seemed frightened and reluctant to make friends or to establish close ties. About nine months prior to admission she and her husband visited her home in South Carolina and following her return to Chicago she began to be more depressed and lonely. At the time of their return from the South, her husband increased his work and was absent from home more than usual. As Christmas of 1955 approached he was busy because of the holiday rush and the patient felt more lonely and frightened. In September of 1955, the patient's only child, a daughter age six, started school. It is noteworthy that the patient herself was six years old when her own mother died. The patient's husband noticed that every six years she has had some emotional difficulty. Twelve years ago she was hospitalized for "hysteria" but the details are not known. In 1949, six years prior to the onset of the current reaction, at the time of the birth of her daughter, she was hospitalized for depression.

In addition there had been a good deal of illness in her family in the late fall and winter of 1944 and 1946. Her sister had a hysterectomy a few weeks prior to the patient's hospitalization. A brother-in-law had an orchidectomy within the last two months for carcinoma of the testes.

Christmastime had always been stressful for her, increasing her longing for her family in the South. This year the feelings of lone-liness and separation from the family were more acute than usual. There also had been some recent difficulty between the patient and an elderly female neighbor with whom she had become fairly close.

In addition to evidences of depression the patient showed memory defect, a type of thinking and confusion which resembled a syndrome of organic brain disease, but this could not be demonstrated. There was also some bizarreness and interference with thought processes which suggested more ego disorganization than was apparent on the surface.

We again find it impossible to understand clearly the development of the current illness either in terms of being able to isolate the precipitating experiences, or to trace the dynamic process.

Case 9

A fifty-six-year-old woman of Jewish upper-middle-class background with fourth-grade education was admitted because she was depressed, agitated, sleepless, and felt that she was going to pieces and was unable to carry on. For this patient, the identification of a crucial experience seems fairly simple. A few months prior to admission the family business owned by the patient and her husband was destroyed by fire. This business consisted of two parts, a hardware store and a large heating and hot water equipment supply depot. The hardware store where the patient worked was completely destroyed and the other part damaged considerably. The fire occurred on a Monday night when ordinarily the store would have been open and the fire discovered and put out sooner, but the patient had changed the "open night" to Friday to conform with changing local custom. Also, that day she had ordered the burning of refuse, which might have been the cause of the fire. Inventory was high at the time because she had stocked heavily to prepare for a steel-strike shortage. Because of this the insurance did not cover the loss. She was convinced that the resulting loss wiped out the family finances. Her husband indicates that this was not true.

Shortly after the fire the patient began to lose her appetite. Some two weeks after the fire, while they were salvaging what they could of the store and the equipment, she began to become suspicious that the employees were looting the store. She recognized that these accusations were inappropriate and apologized to one employee. It was at this time that she became sleepless and demanded attention from her husband during the night. She changed from a sober, adequate working partner to a suspicious detractor of her husband. In the hospital she seemed overtly delusional, being convinced that the whole family future was ruined by her actions and that the interviewer was getting information to hurt her and her family even more.

A previous depression had occurred some six years previously, when the internal revenue service found that she was concealing income in order to pay off loans for expansion of the business. She then made a suicide attempt and was hospitalized but responded adequately to electric shock treatment.

Here the precipitating experience seemed clear; the dynamics, however, remained somewhat speculative. The fire may represent the expression of her angry destructive impulses toward her husband, partly related to her feelings about his inadequacy in business. Traditionally, however, her great personal investment in the business may represent hoarding tendencies which as defenses against depression were wiped out by the fire, leaving her empty and lost.

SUMMARY

Q-sorts of stereotypes of depression held by the investigators, to serve as an added control, revealed a commonly held stereotype very similar to the total composite trait pattern of the patients utilized in the pilot study. The stereotype was almost identical with

Factor A of feelings and concerns and it alone. The fact that the correlations of the stereotype sorts were higher than those of the patients and that patients also fell into two other factors (B and C) indicates that psychiatrists to some extent were able to control and ignore their stereotypes in order to make ratings of the characteristics of particular patients. On the other hand there was much less agreement among the sorts of current behavior stereotypes and less correlation with the total composite of this trait list. In fact two factors were elicited from sorts of stereotypes of current behavior (Alpha and Beta) with mixtures indicating lack of agreement. This disagreement among psychiatrists over stereotypes, in view of the lack of data elicited for "current behavior" ratings, probably intensifies the unreliability in ratings of particular patients. For if data have to be filled in by stereotypes and these are varied, then the resulting ratings will show great variance. Frequency counts of symptoms also reveal the breadth of stereotypes, and show an interesting priority list of symptoms.

Analyses of check lists concerned with dreams, premorbid personality, psychodynamics, and precipitating causes were not fruitful due to lack of information for the first two and absence of consensus for the others. The difficulties inherent in such determination are exemplified by several case vignettes. The case with which precipitating causes are concluded and psychodynamic formulations made by psychiatrists teaching in case conferences or reporting conclusions in the literature is in contrast with the lack of consensus when several competent investigators discuss these questions for the purpose of scientfic inquiry.

CHAPTER 6

Methodology of the Full-Scale Study

THE RESULTS OF OUR PILOT STUDY PROVED OF VALUE in themselves, giving us considerable information of a positive nature, especially regarding factors of feelings and concerns and psychiatrists' stereotypes. In addition, our checklists informed us of the hierarchy of symptoms. We also learned how difficult it was to determine precipitating factors and psychodynamics with any degree of certainty from diagnostic interviews. Finally, we discovered the surprising fact that for a variety of reasons psychiatrists, who sometimes presume to count themselves among behavioral scientists, were actually poor observers and describers of behavior.

CHANGES IN METHOD SUGGESTED BY THE PILOT STUDY

Nevertheless, the pilot study made us confident that meaningful results could be obtained from further studies and encouraged us to begin a full-scale investigation with a modified design and significant alteration in our methods. Not the least of reasons for this shift was the 12 to 15 man-hours of time required to interview and observe each patient for the details set forth in our preliminary inquiry in addition to the time necessary for individual Q-sorts. This technique did not lend itself to a large-scale evaluation.

We had gone through the laborious process of establishing two trait lists and pruning them down to manageable proportions and had extracted three factors from the residue. Thus we already had a preliminary idea of some categories of depression embedded in the global syndrome, but the number of patients (21) from which these factors were derived was much too small for further fractionization. A study of a large series of patients could confirm or deny the presence of the factors obtained in the pilot study and also identify more factors that could not be extracted from a limited number of patients.

Thus, it became necessary to change our experimental design. This meant (1) considerable reduction in size and alteration in content of our trait lists, (2) altering the form of interviewing, (3) changing the source of information necessary for an adequate estimation of behavior and increasing the group of interviewers, (4) altering the method of selecting research subjects and including the study of other control groups, and (5) shifting from the Q-sort rating method to the use of two check lists which are described below.

REVISED PROCEDURE

We selected the top 20 traits from Factors A and B and the top and bottom 10 traits from Factor C, which had been the only bipolar factor, containing patients characterized by both extremes. Using these traits we compiled a check list, with a rating scale from 0 (not present) through 1, 2, and 3 (slightly, moderately, and markedly present). Omitting duplicate traits in the three factors, we ended up with a check list of 47 items each of which was to be rated on a four-point scale. This seemed adequate for our purposes and simple enough to be used by a larger group of people who were not directly involved in the research work. We fully recognized that there would be some loss in omitting the less characteristic traits falling in the intermediate range of the original factors.

All statements of the traits were worked over so that none could be considered double-barreled—that is, stating two things at the same time. About an equal number of questions were expected to receive *yes* and *no* answers. Thus the lists of traits were not only shortened by subtractions, but additions and clarifications were also made.

The interviews were not conducted as a separate activity apart from the routine hospital diagnostic study, and observers listening and viewing the interview from behind a one-way screen were not utilized as in the pilot study. The high reliability in the initial study made this unnecessary for the rating of feelings and concerns. However, to be sure of reliability within the expanded group, four of the original investigators rated feelings and concerns on that check list, after interviewing the patient, for one out of every four patients.

In the pilot study the current behavior studied did not produce correlations sufficiently high to do factor analyses. Hence we had no factors whose traits could be used to construct a check list. Therefore, after reviewing our current behavior and symptom lists, we restated the behavioral traits in a clearer form which could be answered by a *yes* or *no*. We separated these traits into rough categories, such as "affective behavior," "cognitive behavior," "somatic behavioral manifestations," etc. In the strict confines of the psychiatric interview we had not been able to see or recognize "behavioral" manifestations. It became obvious that the people who should be most competent to make such observations and judgments are psychiatric nurses and residents, who are constantly exposed to patients' behavior during the entire twenty-four hours and who are trained in descriptive recording. We enlisted their cooperation in the project and asked the head nurse and the resident assigned to the patient (the resident having already completed the feelings and concerns list after his psychiatric work-up) *jointly* to complete the behavioral check list within five days after the patient's admission.

As a control for these studies, in addition to having the research group see one out of four patients, we asked all members of the research core group and the temporary resident staff additions to fill out the feelings and concerns check list for their concept of a "typical" depression, which we termed their stereotype. All the residents and head nurses also completed the current behavior check list in a similar manner. This gave us a control and a base line against which we could make future comparisons.

Our early studies revealed that the symptom and dream check lists were not productive and that precipitating events and their meanings could not be isolated. We therefore decided to include symptoms in the current behavior check list. Interviewers were requested to ask specific questions about precipitating events and to make simple declarative statements about no more than three precipitating events at the end of the feelings and concerns list.

In the earlier study we selected patients who were diagnosed on admission as depressed by the attending and resident psychiatrists. This required modification because not only did we desire a broad spectrum of depressions to obtain the maximum possible number of factors, but also we wanted to include those patients in a borderline position between depression and other illnesses.

We continued to accept for the study every patient admitted to PPI with the diagnosis of depression, but used the final discharge diagnosis for a separation of patients into groups. This immediately gave us two categories of importance in exploring the borderline area between depression and other disorders. Some patients who were admitted with a diagnosis of depression were discharged as depressed. Some patients were admitted as depressions but discharged with another diagnosis. It was important to utilize the latter group, because something about these patients had suggested the diagnosis of depression on admission to the hospital but, after subsequent study, this diagnosis was revised.

We also used a group of nondepressed patients as a control in order to see whether any of the factors in depression could be found. This gave us a third small category and, unexpectedly, a fourth group admitted to the hospital with diagnoses other than depression, some of whom were discharged with a diagnosis of depression. We anticipated that careful study of differences in these four groups might be revealing.

The two new check lists are presented in Tables 25 and 26. The statistical methods of analyzing the data will be explained in the following chapter dealing with results.

Protocol for the Depression Study

The following instructions were drawn up for the interviewers and raters:

1. Before beginning to work up patients for this research, each resident and member of the research group will be asked to complete a feelings and concerns check list about his stereotype of a depressed patient. Each resident and head nurse will be asked to complete the current behavior check list for his or her behavioral stereotype of the depressed patient.

2. Patients will be selected for the project by the coordinator. Criteria will be a diagnosis of "depression" or "depressive reaction" as the major pathology by both the attending psychiatrist and the resident psychiatrist who admits the patient. Every patient entering PPI during the term of the study with these diagnoses will be included, unless special circumstances arise to prevent this. Should this occur, the coordinator will take precautions to randomize the selection procedure.

3. A copy of the feelings and concerns check list with the patient's name and research number on it will be placed in the mailbox of the resident who has been assigned to work up this patient. This list should be completed within 48 hours of admission and returned to the coordinator.

4. A copy of the feelings and concerns check list will also be placed in the mailbox of one of the members of the research group for every fourth patient. Assignments to this group will be made in rotation by the project coordinator. The member of the research group will see the patient within 48 hours, complete the checklist, and return it to the coordinator's mailbox.

5. Within the first five days of each patient's hospitalization, the coordinator will deliver to the head nurse of the unit a copy of the current behavior check list. After the patient has been in the hospital

for five days, the head nurse and the resident psychiatrist assigned to the patient will, together, complete this list. Since the questions on this list are about observable behavior, requiring minimal interpretation, it is assumed that the nurse and resident can arrive at agreement about answers to specific questions. Any and all available material about the patient's behavior, including nurses' notes, reports from aides and attendants, and occupational therapy notes, should be used to provide information from which to answer the questions on the check list.

6. The completed current behavior list should be returned to the project coordinator.

Preliminary Questions

Before beginning the full study, we set down nine preliminary questions that we hoped could be extracted from the analysis of the new data:

1. Do the evaluations made by the residents correlate with those made by members of the research group?
   a. Are their stereotypes similar?
   b. Are differences in resident stereotypes correlated with experience and level of training? If the intercorrelations are not good, is this due to the inclusion of a small group (for example, the first-year residents) that may be quite divergent from the rest?
   c. Can we use the resident evaluations with the same degree of security as those of the research group who are known to correlate well with each other?
2. With regard to the feelings and concerns list, is the presence of the three factors found in the pilot study confirmed or denied?
   a. If the factors are confirmed does the analysis of data indicate that there are yet undiscovered factors too weak to have made their presence known in the pilot investigations?
   b. If the existence of other factors is suggested, can we find them in this larger group?

    c. Are there marked differences in numbers of patients who show different symptoms?

3. With regard to the current behavior list, which has not been previously factored, can we find separate and distinct behavioral patterns?

    a. Do the stereotypes of the residents and head nurses who made these behavioral ratings correlate with each other?

    b. Again, if the correlations are not good, is this the result of a small group who diverge widely from the rest?

    c. If factors describing behavior can be found, do they correlate with particular "content" factors in the feelings and concerns sample?

4. Is there a correlation between any of the factors in the feelings and concerns or current behavior samples with demographic items such as age, sex, religion, social status, presence of physical disease, etc.?

5. Are there correlations between the phenomena of the disease as described by our factors and the nature of the precipitating experience? (Using broad categories, e.g., death of a loved one, moving, loss of job, etc.)

6. What inferences are suggested or documented about the relationship between the raters' stereotype and the description of patients?

7. Do those patients who were initially diagnosed "depression" but discharged with some other diagnosis, constitute a special and distinct group having characteristics of its own, and/or does this group lie in a borderline area between depression and other illnesses?

8. Do those patients who were admitted with a diagnosis other than depression but who were discharged as "depressed" also constitute a special group?

9. Do we find the factors described in depressed patients in our control series?

TABLE 25

FEELINGS AND CONCERNS CHECK LIST

Patient's Name _____ Patient's #__Age__Sex__Race__
Marital Status_____ Occupation_____ Education_____
Rated by:_____Attending Psychiatrist_____

Each of the traits below should be rated in one of
the four columns:

0 - Not present in this patient
    Present to:
1 - Slight extent
2 - Moderate extent
3 - Marked extent

	0	1	2	3
1. Feels hopeless				
2. Feels that he (she) is being brave in bearing troubles				
3. Can laugh at times				
4. Feels helpless and powerless				
5. Has feelings of tenseness				
6. Feels he (she) is being persecuted				
7. Concerned with suffering caused to others				
8. Feels that illness would be relieved by the solving of certain "material" problems— money, job, housing, etc.				
9. Feelings are dominated by sadness and "blueness"				
10. Feels self unworthy				
11. Considers self lazy				
12. Feels optimistic				
13. Feels loss of interest in "oral satisfactions" —food, drink, smoking				
14. Expresses much concern for the welfare of family and friends				
15. Feels he (she) brought illness on self				
16. Has ideas of committing suicide				
17. Concerned with material loss—money, property, etc.				
18. Increased sexual feelings and interests				
19. Feels constantly fatigued				
20. Feels "at end of rope"				
21. Wants to cry much of the time				

(Continued)

125

TABLE 25 *(Continued)*

	0	1	2	3
22. Feels envious of others				
23. Experiences free anxiety				
24. Feels hopeful about getting better				
25. Feels a failure				
26. Concerned with aging and lessening vigor				
27. Concerned with making up for wrongs to others				
28. Gets much secondary gain from illness				
29. Feels guilt for not assuming family and/or job responsibilities				
30. Anger that is present attached to unreasonable objects				
31. Guilt feelings experienced				
32. Feels unable to make decisions				
33. Has anxiety about particular concerns				
34. Feels loss of esteem by others				
35. Feels that the illness was precipitated by recent events				
36. Feels unloved				
37. Experiences moodiness				
38. Feels burdened by the demands of others				
39. Professes to have little or no feelings				
40. Concern over increasing sexual interest				
41. Feels "jittery"				
42. Feels relieved after hospitalization				
43. Feels unable to act				
44. Shame is experienced				
45. Feels ambivalent toward important personal issues				
46. Feels lonely				
47. Credits illness to excessive family and/or job responsibility				

This patient became depressed because of:

_____ and

_____ and

_____ and . . .

TABLE 26

CURRENT BEHAVIOR CHECK LIST

Patient # _____

On the following list please indicate whether each statement is to be answered "Yes" or "No" for this patient and check the appropriate column. Please answer all items using the list.

Patient's Name _____ Age___ Race_____
Marital Status _____ Religion _____ Date of Admission_____
Sex ____ Date of this report _____Attending Psychiatrist _____
Form filled out by: Head Nurse _____ Resident _____

I Affective Behavior	Yes	No
1. Complains of being sad and blue		
2. Complains of boredom		
3. Cries (lacrimation)		
4. Sobs (no lacrimation)		
5. Restless (has difficulty in remaining still)		
6. Never smiles		
7. Seen to smile at some time during observation		
8. Reports feeling cheerful		
9. Destroys objects or strikes at people		
10. Complains of having been provoked or of becoming angry		
11. Shouts, raises voice, or uses derogatory language		
12. Complains of being suspicious of staff or other patients		
13. Complains of being anxious		
14. Overtly anxious (shows any of these: widened palpebral fissure, dilated pupils, moist palms, tremor, tense facial musculature)		
15. Complains of being unable to cry		
16. Shows evidence of humor (responds appropriately to humorous situations and/or can make other people laugh)		
17. Composed		
18. Provokes anger in staff or patients		
19. Flirtatious		
20. Shows off body or possessions		
21. Appears in lounge in state of undress		

(Continued)

127

TABLE 26 *(Continued)*

	Yes	No
22. Wide fluctuations and variability in behavior		
23. Witty and charming		
24. Wide and rapid mood changes		
25. Unconvincing gaiety		
II Cognitive Behavior		
26. Well oriented for time, place, and person		
27. Has obvious hallucinations		
28. Has obvious delusions		
29. States the environment is not real		
30. States that he (she) feels unreal		
31. Misidentifies people		
32. Memory is good		
33. Impairment of recent memory		
34. Impairment of remote memory		
35. Acts as though he (she) understands what is said to him (her)		
36. Acts as though he (she) understands the hospital environment		
37. States he (she) is confused		
38. Cannot concentrate		
39. Talks of strange and unusual ideas or fantasies (If *yes*, specify)		
40. Has distorted sense of time		
41. Thought processes are slow and retarded		
42. Limited and repetitive thought content		
III Somatic Behavioral Manifestations		
A. Gastrointestinal		
43. Appetite poor		
44. Increased appetite		
45. Craving for special foods		
46. Nauseated		
47. Vomits		
48. Has diarrhea (since onset of illness)		
49. Is constipated (since onset of illness)		
50. Shows bloating and belching		
51. Eats with group in lounge		
52. Eats at frequent intervals between meals		
53. Eats breakfast		

(Continued)

TABLE 26 *(Continued)*

	Yes	No
54. Eats lunch		
55. Eats dinner		
56. Eats alone in room		
B. Genitourinary		
57. Shows marked interest in opposite sex		
58. Shows little or no interest in opposite sex		
C. Dermatological		
59. Has excessively dry skin		
60. Has dry hair and scalp; difficulty in combing hair		
61. Recent change in skin color		
62. Change in hair color		
63. Sweating increased		
64. Sweating decreased		
65. Has specific skin lesions or eruptions		
D. Sleep Behavior		
66. Difficulty in getting to sleep		
67. Wakefulness during the night		
68. Wakes very early in the morning		
69. Required sedation for sleep after the first 48 hours of hospitalization		
70. Sleeps during the day		
71. Sleeps excessively		
E. Psychomotor Activity and Behavior		
72. Gait and general behavior slow and retarded		
73. Paces floor		
74. Wrings hands		
75. Sits alone very quietly		
76. Stays in bed much of the time		
77. Constantly active		
78. Assumes unusual postures		
79. Changes tasks frequently		
80. Has flat, masklike face		
81. Picks at self or clothing		
82. Is dramatic and theatrical		
83. Holds self stiff and rigid		

(Continued)

TABLE 26 *(Continued)*

	Yes	No
84. Has ticlike movements		
85. Is easily distractable		
86. Tremulous		
F. Speech		
87. Volume of voice decreased		
88. Slurred and mumbled		
89. Slowed and retarded		
90. Rapid and accelerated		
91. Stilted and artificial		
92. Sighs		
G. Head and Sense Organs		
93. Has headaches		
94. Complains of troubles with eyes		
95. Especially sensitive to noise		
96. Has bad taste in mouth		
97. Dizzy spells		
H. Care of Self		
98. Clean and neat		
99. Dresses appropriately		
100. Pays attention to grooming		
IV Communicative Behavior		
101. Communicates easily and well		
102. Communicates with staff		
103. Communicates with other patients		
104. Makes excessive demands		
105. Clinging		
106. Requests center around medication or physical treatments		
107. Complains frequently of somatic symptoms		
108. Enters into activity with group on unit		
109. Isolated and withdrawn		
110. Prefers to remain by him(her)self		
111. Becomes a leader in unit activities		
112. Follows others' suggestions passively ("goes along")		

(Continued)

TABLE 26 *(Continued)*

	Yes	No
113. Complains constantly about hospital, staff, food, etc.		
114. Seems pleased by facilities and care in the hospital		
115. Expresses appreciation for care and interest of staff		
116. Is disruptive of group activities		
117. Disruptive of staff attention to other patients		
118. Becomes part of a small clique		
119. Feels more comfortable after hospitalization		
120. Feels less comfortable after hospitalization		
121. Acts ingratiatingly with staff		
122. Tries to ''do good'' for other patients and to help the staff with their work		
123. Seems alert and responsive		
124. Relates in a distant and guarded manner		
125. Communicates with men		
126. Communicates with women		
V General Behavior		
127. Evidence of suicidal thoughts or behavior		
128. Response to similar situations varies		
129. Expresses need for help		
130. Approaches other people as a source of help		
VI Behavior in Occupational Therapy		
131. Difficulty in starting projects		
132. Difficulty in completing projects		
133. Becomes involved in detail		
134. Little attention to detail		
135. Works primarily by himself		
136. Makes realistic demands of personnel		
137. Avoids using color in work; uses dark, somber colors		
138. Uses bright vivid colors		
VII Physical Examination		
139. Physical examination is essentially negative		

If the answer to question No. 139 is *no* please list below the significant physical findings.

CHAPTER 7

Factor Analysis of Feelings
and Concerns Check List

THE ANALYSIS PRESENTED IN THIS CHAPTER GREW
out of an earlier pilot study in which psychiatrists made Q-sort
ratings of 21 patients on 111 traits relating to the feelings and
concerns of depressed patients. Twenty cases were intercorrelated
(Q-correlations) and factor-analyzed. Three prominent factors
were found, which were labeled A, B, and C respectively. Although the meanings of the factors seemed relatively clear and it
was difficult to restrain ourselves from making interpretations, it
was decided to withhold judgment about the factors until they
were verified by a more extensive study, described in this chapter.

STATISTICAL METHOD USED IN ANALYZING THE DATA

Subsequent to the pilot factor analysis, the 111 feelings and
concerns traits were reduced to 47, which included the traits most
highly loaded on the factors A, B, and C. The 47 traits were
then used in a check list. A four-point rating scale was used for
each trait, ranging from 0 ("not present in this patient") to 4
("present to a marked extent").

Check-list ratings were made of 120 patients, of whom 96 were
both admitted and discharged as depressive (B-D), 8 were ad-

132

mitted as depressive and discharged as other than depressive (D-O), 6 were admitted as other than depressive and discharged as depressive (O-D), and 10 were other syndromes (O-O), neither admitted nor discharged as depressive. Our first analysis concerns only the 96 patients both admitted and discharged as depressive.

All of the patients were rated by resident psychiatrists who had ample opportunity to observe patients and talk with them on the wards. Five psychiatrists on the research team made ratings of 24 of the patients. The analysis to be described concerned only the rating made by residents attending the 96 patients who were both admitted and discharged as depressed. Comparisons will be made later of ratings made by residents and by members of the research team.

The raw data consisted of 96 patients rated on 47 traits. All of the ratings were placed on IBM punched cards and then transferred to digital computer tape. The items (traits) were intercorrelated on the digital computer, resulting in a 47-by-47 matrix of 1,081 correlation coefficients. The matrix was factor-analyzed in several steps. First, three "group centroids" were formed to represent the three factors found in the pilot study. Loadings were computed on the three group centroids. A square-root factoring was then done on the three group centroids, using unities in the diagonal spaces. This successively orthogonalized group centroid B from A, and then C from both A and B. This procedure serves to test whether the three factors found in the pilot study are present in the current study, and the result provides a measure of the extent to which each of the 47 items belongs to each of the three factors. The three factors which were found will be designated I, II, and III respectively.

After obtaining the three factors in this way, an effort was made to find additional factors. The variance due to the three orthogonal factors was extracted from the original matrix. The highest residual coefficient in each column was placed in the diagonal space. Six centroid factors were extracted from the residual matrix. The six factors were rotated by both "Quartimax" and "Varimax" procedures (factors I, II, and III were not included in the rotations). The "Varimax" produced the most interpretable solution, the results of which will be described.

The roles of persons and items in this study are reversed from that of the first study. In the first study there were only 21 persons (patients) and 111 items (traits). Consequently, it was more convenient to intercorrelate and factor-analyze persons. In the resulting solution, factor loadings were given to persons, and factor scores were given to traits. In this analysis, factor loadings are given to items, and factor scores are given to persons.

The practice was adopted of listing only those items with loadings of .40 or larger, except that in several cases it was necessary to list some of the items with loadings slightly below .40 in order to have sufficient content for factor interpretation.

The results are very good in that the statistical solution and the interpretability of the factors could hardly be better. In respect to statistics. Factors I, II, and III have high loadings, surprisingly high for items rated on a four-point scale. There are only three items that load strongly on Factor II, but two of these loadings are quite high, and even item 4, with the lowest loading, fits in very well with the content of the others.

In respect to interpretability, there are striking resemblances between the content of I here and A from the pilot study, II here and B in the pilot study, and III here and C in the pilot study. Where the two sets of factors differ in item content, it serves to make the factors here more pure and more interpretable than their respective counterparts in the pilot study.

Of the six additional factors, only one of them, Factor IV, is statistically strong. The content is rather clear; as a trait cluster it is concerned with anxiety, which might have been expected to comprise a large element in depressions. Factor V is also a useful dimension. In it only two traits are outstanding (with loadings above .50) but there are four traits with loadings in the .30's. The remaining four factors are not strong enough to take seriously.

Present evidence thus indicates that there are five prominent factors in the ratings of feelings and concerns by the psychiatric staff. Three of the factors are confirmed by the earlier pilot investigation. This is an important type of support because the two studies differed in a number of ways: different rating methods, different numbers of traits being rated, different raters, and ratings made with different kinds of observations and information. This provides some confidence that the factors are not simply artifacts of certain particularities of research methods and procedures.

A very useful by-product of the analysis is that it demonstrates that at least some of the traits in the 47-item list can be rated reliably by the psychiatric residents. Unreliable rating could not have produced the high correlations and high factor loadings which were found.

INTERPRETATION OF THE FACTORS ELICITED

We shall now attempt to "interpret" the five factors with the recognition that our inferences, not always reaching consensus, are not the only ones that can be made and that in reality they constitute *hypotheses* to be further tested. One over-all suggestion was made that Factor I, including expressions of hopelessness, sadness, failure, feelings of unworthiness, and indecisiveness, was an index of the "degree" or "amount" of depression, since this factor seemed to show affects and self-concepts in a quantifiable manner. Factors II, III, and V then could be further defined as "types" of depression, since their traits revealed some ways of handling affects or conflicts in relation to the subjects' inner and outer worlds.

Factor I: In general the high loading traits express a dismal affect, hopelessness, loss of self-esteem, and a self-image of badness. Shame and guilt feelings seem not expressed as primary but as secondary reactions to the nuclear concept of unworthiness. Considered from the frame of regression initiated by some internal or external events, the accretion of ego illusions may have been weak-

Factor I

Rank	Loading*	Item No.	Item
1	.815	20	Feels "at end of rope"
2	.798	1	Feels hopeless
3	.761	9	Feelings are dominated by sadness and "blueness"
4	.731	4	Feels helpless and powerless
5	.709	25	Feels a failure
6	.660	10	Feels self unworthy
7	.638	11	Considers self lazy
8	.603	43	Feels unable to act
9	.581	29	Feels guilt for not assuming family and/or job responsibilities
10	.580	32	Feels unable to make decisions

* Loadings here are expressed to three decimal places for greater accuracy. The word "loading" is simply another word for correlation. A loading indicates the extent to which an item correlates with a factor.

ened and, in the absence of other effective ego mechanisms of defense, the core process becomes exposed. The revealed bad-self and self-punishment suggests according to Benedek's thesis that these patients had greater than usual frustrations or alimentary problems in the phase of mother-child symbiosis.

Factor II

Rank	Loading	Item No.	Item
1	.787	8	Feels that illness would be relieved by the solving of certain "material" problems—money, job, housing, etc.
2	.748	17	Concerned with material loss—money, property, etc.
3	.562	38	Feels burdened by the demands of others
4	.384	47	Credits illness to excessive family and/or job responsibility

Factor II corresponds with Factor B of the pilot study, which was significantly higher in males. The almost complete concern with external problems can be viewed either as precedent or subsequent to the depression. In seems more plausible to consider these references to external events as evidences of a *projective defense* for which men have ample opportunity to rationalize in view of ubiquitous work conflicts. These patients are less sick than Factor I patients just because they can utilize projection as a defense, which at the same time indicates a degree of hopefulness that the external world which they have not abandoned will eventually supply them with necessary satisfactions, a hope not available to those in Factor I.

Factor III

Rank	Loading	Item No.	Item
1	.737	27	Concerned with making up for wrongs to others
2	.702	14	Expresses much concern for the welfare of family and friends
3	.687	7	Concerned with suffering caused to others
4	.655	31	Guilt feelings experienced
5	.513	29	Feels guilty for not assuming family and/or job responsibilities
6	.429	15	Feels he (she) brought illness on self
7	.413	44	Shame is experienced

Patients described by Factor III experience severe feelings of guilt associated with strong wishes and efforts to make restitution. The restitutive efforts suggest a better prognosis for the subjects, who, although with considerable difficulty, still are concerned with relating to human objects. The patients within this category give the impression that they are struggling with guilt feelings over unconscious aggressions directed toward significant objects or their images. It is toward these that restitutive efforts are made.

Factor IV

Rank	Loading	Item No.	Item
1	.736	5	Has feelings of tenseness
2	.734	23	Experiences free anxiety
3	.700	41	Feels "jittery"
4	.417	33	Has anxiety about particular concerns

The items in the Factor IV list together constitute a pure culture of anxiety and may correspond to the agitation found in many patients, if not all, at some level. The question is how much anxiety develops in individual patients or in patients within other factors. Another hypothesis worthy of consideration is that the anxiety factor is present in greatest intensity in patients who are in the process of going in or out of depression.

Factor V

Rank	Loading	Item No.	Item
1	.593	36	Feels unloved
2	.541	28	Gets much secondary gain from illness
3	.378	2	Feels that he (she) is being brave in bearing troubles
4	.361	30	Anger that is present attached to unreasonable object
5	.360	22	Feels envious of others
6	.330	46	Feels lonely

Factor V describes a patient who feels unloved and correspondingly inferior and envious. The traits indicate that the precipitation of illness has been some cue that to them means they are not sufficiently loved or that they have been rejected. They are angry and attempt to force their objects to give them excessive interest and attention. The clinging demanding attitude only thinly hides the anger under a martyred posture. From these processes some satisfaction is attained which leads to a fixation on the secondary gain.

Still further interpretive efforts regarded Factor I as a general quantitative index of depressed mood and the other factors as defenses or attempted resolutions of the depression. Factor II thus can be viewed as a resolution of aggressive (oral incorporative) impulses by projection to the outside world; Factor III as an expression of guilt over aggression with attempted resolution by restitutive activity or fantasy; Factor IV as an expression of anxiety, which might be a transient or intermediate phase during the alignment of defensive operations; and Factor V as the "love addict," needing supplies and attempting to manipulate and force the external world into providing them. Here each of the factors shows both an antecedent impulse or wish and a resultant ego defense. These suggestions as attempts at setting up hypotheses should be viewed in the light of current concepts of ego psychology, understandable as behaviors resulting from an interplay and resolution of conflict. However, the alternative hypothesis for Factor I as an end stage of regression or as a quantitative variance of loss of self-esteem needs also to be considered.

FACTOR-ANALYTIC RESULTS: QUESTIONS AND CONCLUSIONS

Although the confirmation of our previous factors and the clear emergence of the current ones was gratifying, there were some important unanswered questions. Some traits which our clinical experience suggested should or might appear in a categorization of depression did not show up on any factor. We were especially concerned about the following 7 traits and questioned why none of these traits appeared in any of our factors:

13. Feels loss of interest in "oral satisfactions"
16. Has ideas of committing suicide
19. Feels constantly fatigued
21. Wants to cry much of the time
34. Feels loss of esteem by others

42. Feels relieved after hospitalization

45. Feels ambivalent toward important personal issues

We wondered whether some traits might be too "universal" to factor out. Subsequent calculations of the means and standard deviations showed that these traits simply were not covariant with others so as to form any patterning, and thus had to be regarded as not characteristic of a *special* category.

The next step in the analysis was to obtain scores for each of the patients on each of the feelings and concerns factors. The resulting scores presented a number of facts and posed a number of new questions. Among the facts, it was found that the patients varied interestingly in two ways: (1) some had high scores on particular factors, and some had low scores; and (2) some patients were characterized by (were high on) only one or two of the factors, and other patients were high on several or all of the factors. Table 27 shows the factor loadings, means, and standard deviations for each of the items in the feelings and concerns check list. Table 28 shows the average scores for 96 patients within each factor.

We have some questions about several aspects of these scores. Do patients who score low on all factors indicate that still other factors may be present to account for them, or does this mean that these patients were not depressed? Also, the relationship between factors such as I and IV, which means between depressed affect and anxiety, would be extremely interesting and might lead to some further ideas about what the interrelationships between these factors mean. The scores permit us to select those people who are high in a single factor or combination of factors for further research and enable us to prepare a set of selection criteria to pick up, at the time of admission, patients who belong in one or another factor.

The 96 patients who were both admitted and discharged as depressed, symbolized by D-D, have been described. Subsequently, scores on the five feelings and concerns factors were found for three other small groups of patients: (1) a group of 8 patients who were diagnosed initially as depressive and were later diagnosed as not being depressive (D-O); (2) a group of 6 patients diagnosed initially as not depressive and later diagnosed as depressive (O-D); and (3) a group of 10 patients who were diagnosed initially and later as not being depressive (O-O).

The average factor scores for all four groups are listed in Table 29. Because of the small number of cases in the non-D-D groups, the results are only suggestive. Scores on Factors I and IV interact very nicely. We suggested previously that Factor I indicates the amount of depression and the other factors indicate the kind of depression. The results support this very well. The D-D patients are high on Factor I (depressed affect) and high on Factor IV (anxiety). The O-D patients are high on Factor I but low in anxiety (Factor IV). Apparently the relatively low anxiety level induced a nondepressive diagnosis originally. The D-O group (pseudodepressives) are relatively low in Factor I and relatively high in IV (anxiety). They should not have been diagnosed depressive. This suggests that psychiatrists look for anxiety as a crucial component in depression, and, if they do not find it, the diagnosis tends to be not depression, but some other psychiatric entity with components of depressed mood. Conversely, if the patient shows anxiety, and even if Factor I is relatively low, the diagnosis is depression. It further suggests that anxiety (Factor IV) is a usual concomitant of depression but by no means necessary, since there are cases, like those in the O-D group, with relatively low anxiety who, on more careful examination, prove to be depressive.

SUMMARY

Check-list ratings were made of 120 patients, of whom 96 were admitted with the diagnosis of depression and so discharged (D-D), 8 admitted as depressive and discharged as other than depressive (D-O), 6 admitted as other than depressive and discharged as depressive (O-D) and 10 were other syndromes (O-O). Five relatively strong factors were found, the first three of which were identical to the three factors found in the feelings and concerns list of the pilot study. As to interpretation, the strong Factor I may be an index of the degree of depression or a quantitative index and the other factors indicators of types differentiated by varying attempts at defense and resolution of depression.

Thus Factor I describes the dismal, hopeless, self-castigating person; II, the person who attributes his depression to external events or persons; III, the person with powerful guilty feelings over aggressions who is attempting restitution; IV, the almost pure culture of the anxiety-laden person; and V, the clinging, demanding, and angry person.

The D-D patients were high in depressed mood and anxiety, the O-D patients were high in depressed mood and low in anxiety, the D-O were low in depressed mood but high in anxiety, and the O-O patients were low in all factors except for clinging dependency, which could mean the dependency of almost any newly admitted mental hospital patient.

TABLE 27

FACTOR LOADINGS, MEANS, AND STANDARD DEVIATIONS FOR
ITEMS IN THE FEELINGS AND CONCERNS CHECK LIST

Items	Factor Number					x	α
	I	II	III	IV	V		
1. Feels hopeless	.80	-.14	-.17	-.07	.03	1.67	1.01
2. Feels that he (she) is being brave in bearing troubles	-.01	.07	-.01	-.23	.38	1.06	.76
3. Can laugh at times	-.32	.14	.11	.10	.06	1.23	.86
4. Feels helpless and powerless	.73	-.07	-.11	.19	-.07	1.76	.96
5. Has feelings of tenseness	.24	.02	.28	.74	.05	2.26	.75
6. Feels he (she) is being persecuted	.33	.03	.14	.02	.12	.43	.70
7. Concerned with suffering	.36	.13	.69	-.01	-.07	1.07	.97
8. Feels that illness would be relieved by the solving of certain "material" problems—money, job, housing, etc.	.08	.79	-.01	-.07	-.09	.81	1.03
9. Feelings are dominated by sadness and "blueness"	.76	.04	.08	-.02	.05	1.84	.93
10. Feels self unworthy	.66	.03	.26	.10	.06	1.37	.98
11. Considers self lazy	.64	.09	.23	.04	-.19	.78	1.01
12. Feels optimistic	-.33	-.01	.10	-.02	.07	.80	.75
13. Feels loss of interest in "oral satisfactions"—food, drink, smoking	.42	.02	.02	-.20	-.23	1.74	1.05
14. Expresses much concern for the welfare of family and friends	.23	.24	.70	-.07	-.15	1.29	1.04
15. Feels he (she) brought illness on self	.51	.27	.43	.01	.18	.81	1.00

(Continued)

TABLE 27 *(Continued)*

Items	Factor Number					x	∝
	I	II	III	IV	V		
16. Has ideas of committing suicide	.29	-.08	.09	-.27	.06	.58	.85
17. Concerned with material loss—money, property, etc.	.20	.75	.06	.19	.02	.69	.92
18. Increased sexual feelings and interests	.14	-.08	-.18	-.08	·.07	.03	.23
19. Feels constantly fatigued	.42	.04	.01	-.24	-.25	1.81	.96
20. Feels "at end of rope"	.82	.04	.06	-.10	-.02	1.56	.96
21. Wants to cry much of the time	.41	-.25	.28	.01	-.06	1.49	1.12
22. Feels envious of others	.19	-.01	.02	-.35	.36	.84	.85
23. Experiences free anxiety	.24	.02	.22	.73	-.13	1.59	1.05
24. Feels hopeful about getting better	-.14	.12	.12	.23	-.11	1.26	.75
25. Feels a failure	.71	.15	.16	.01	.01	1.18	.91
26. Concerned with aging and lessening vigor	.35	.26	.20	.06	.25	1.35	1.11
27. Concerned with making up for wrongs to others	.24	.05	.74	.02	.20	.68	.78
28. Gets much secondary gain from illness	.21	.11	-.02	-.11	.54	1.26	.85
29. Feels guilt for not assuming family and/or job responsibilities	.58	.25	.51	-.02	-.24	1.19	.96
30. Anger that is present attached to unreasonable object	.36	.01	-.01	.14	.36	.91	.89
31. Guilt feelings experienced	.47	.18	.66	.03	.04	1.28	.92
32. Feels unable to make decisions	.58	-.02	.18	.31	.10	1.69	1.05

(Continued)

TABLE 27 *(Continued)*

Items	Factor Number					x	α
	I	II	III	IV	V		
33. Has anxiety about particular concerns	.22	.23	.12	.42	-.28	1.65	.88
34. Feels loss of esteem by others	.36	.25	.08	-.18	-.26	1.21	.88
35. Feels that the illness was precipitated by recent events	.01	.24	.03	-.01	-.04	1.49	1.12
36. Feels unloved	.33	.02	.05	-.17	.59	1.18	.96
37. Experiences moodiness	.30	-.06	.12	.13	-.07	1.82	.78
38. Feels burdened by the demands of others	.19	.56	-.05	-.11	.10	1.26	.89
39. Professes to have little or no feelings	.49	-.15	.15	-.07	.19	.84	1.03
40. Concern over increasing sexual interest	.09	-.11	.19	-.01	-.01	.01	.10
41. Feels "jittery"	.20	.05	.26	.70	-.06	2.02	.91
42. Feels relieved after hospitalization	-.04	.16	.13	.16	.29	1.43	.92
43. Feels unable to act	.60	.01	.11	.29	.21	1.80	.99
44. Shame is experienced	.53	.19	.41	.04	.02	1.29	.88
45. Feels ambivalent toward important personal issues	.42	.03	.13	.01	.11	1.49	.83
46. Feels lonely	.39	.12	.08	-.02	.33	1.64	.82
47. Credits illness to excessive family and/or job responsibility	.13	.38	-.09	.05	.10	.93	1.04

TABLE 28

AVERAGE FEELINGS AND CONCERNS FACTOR SCORES
FOR 96 PATIENTS

Factor	Average Score*
I	1.48
II	.95
III	1.08
IV	1.96
V	1.15

*The average factor scores are reported on the same
scale as the original four-point (0, 1, 2, 3) rating scale.

TABLE 29

AVERAGE SCORES FOR VARIOUS GROUPS ON
THE FEELINGS AND CONCERNS FACTORS

Category	Factor I	Factor II	Factor III	Factor IV	Factor V
D-D Admitted Depressive Discharged Depressive	1.48	0.95	1.08	1.96	1.15
O-D Admitted Other Discharged Depressive	1.40	0.80	1.20	1.20	0.90
D-O Admitted Depressive Discharged Other	0.70	0.80	0.80	1.80	0.90
O-O Admitted Other Discharged Other	1.00	0.70	0.60	1.30	1.20

CHAPTER 8

Reliability Studies of Feelings and Concerns Ratings

THE SUCCESS OF THE DEPRESSION STUDY DEPENDS in large measure on the accuracy of psychiatric ratings which are the basic measurements, and if these prove to be inaccurate this precludes the possibility of finding lawful relationships in the data. The problem is acute in studies of this kind, because the rating task for feelings and concerns involves not only observations, but also inferences which can easily be complicated by preconceptions.

One of the first pilot studies in the depression research was to examine the reliability with which psychiatrists made Q-ratings of 21 patients, the results of which were useful in refining procedures for subsequent large-scale investigations. In the original study all ratings were made by members of the research team; in the full-scale research the bulk of the ratings were made by resident psychiatrists. We now present a study to determine the reliability of the ratings made by residents and to compare the ratings made by them with those made by members of the research team.

COMPARISON OF RELIABILITY OF RATINGS BY
RESIDENTS AND RESEARCH TEAM MEMBERS

There are two kinds of reliability comparisons that can be made: (1) between residents and members of the research team; and (2) among residents separately and among members of the research team separately. In order to make the first type of comparison, each of 23 patients was rated on the 47-item feelings and concerns check list by one of the residents and by one member of the research team. Correlations between the pairs of ratings are presented in Table 30.

After looking at Table 30 it is apparent that agreement between residents and members of the research team is relatively low. The average correlation is only .43, some of the correlations are nil, and one is even negative. There are three possible ways to explain the low correlations. First, it may be that both sets of ratings, residents and research team, are unreliable. Second, it may be that one set of ratings is unreliable and the other is reliable. Third, it may be that both sets of ratings are reliable and residents differ systematically from members of the research team. We have some evidence to indicate which of these is correct.

The major evidence comes from the factor analysis of ratings made by residents where the loadings were generally high. It was remarked that the high loadings indicated good reliability for the ratings made by residents. A more careful study of the reliability of those ratings has now been made. The score for a particular patient on a factor is obtained by adding the ratings given that patient on the items which relate to the factor. The coefficients in Table 31 indicate the reliabilities of the factor scores. It is these factor scores which will be used in making statistical comparisons in the future, and it is primarily important that they be reliable.

The coefficients in Table 31 are generally good. Those for Factors II and V are lower than what one might hope for, but the

TABLE 30

RATINGS BY RESIDENTS AND PSYCHIATRISTS ON THE FEELINGS AND CONCERNS CHECK LIST

Number and Patient	Correlation*	Resident	Psychiatrist
1 (22)	.27	IV	C
2 (23)	.02	V	C
3 (28)	.51	IV	A
4 (29)	.28	III	C
5 (34)	.55	III	E
6 (37)	.21	IX	C
7 (61)	.48	V	A
8 (63)	.52	III	C
9 (64)	.50	IX	B
10 (87)	.44	III	D
11 (88)	.54	V	A
12 (89)	.22	IV	B
13 (108)	.51	II	B
14 (119)	.44	II	E
15 (127)	.27	II	A
16 (133)	.60	V	B
17 (138)	-.19	V	A
18 (145)	.23	V	A
19 (146)	.60	V	E
20 (147)	.07	V	D
21 (153)	.59	V	D
22 (155)	.51	V	E
23 (157)	.42	V	D

*Average intercorrelation equals .43, computed by use of Fisher's Z-transformation.

TABLE 31

RELIABILITY OF FACTOR SCORES
FROM FEELINGS AND CONCERNS CHECK LIST
(RATINGS BY RESIDENTS ONLY)

Factor Number	Reliability (Coefficient Alpha*)
I	.90
II	.61
III	.88
IV	.87#
V	.68

* See Guilford (1954) for mathematics involved
in obtaining these results.

average reliability is .82. This is pretty strong evidence that reliability among residents themselves is relatively good, and consequently the low agreement between residents and members of the research team is not due to the explanation that *both* sets of ratings are unreliable.

In order to support the third explanation above, it would be necessary to show a reliability among members of the research team comparable to that shown in Table 31 for residents. Because in the present study only one member of the research team rated each patient, there are no data directly related to the issue, but some of the results obtained in the earlier study of 21 cases give some strong suggestions. Table 18 shows an average coefficient alpha of .81, almost identical with the average reported here for residents. However, there is one very important difference between the two sets of findings. In the earlier study of members of the research team only, the alphas were computed for the average ratings of *four* psychiatrists. Here the alphas represent the reliabilities of *single* residents.

In Chapter 4 it was stated that correlations between the research team members were not generally high (an average of about .35) and that a high reliability could be obtained only by averaging the ratings of four psychiatrists for each patient. As was pointed out, if only three members of the research team rated each patient, the reliabilities would have in many cases dropped dangerously low. In other words, we find only modest reliability for individual research team members. If subsequent large-scale investigations had been based on ratings by the research team, it would have been necessary to continue using four raters for each patient. In the present study we find that it is necessary to use only one resident to achieve satisfactory reliability.

The evidence points to the second explanation above: the low agreement between residents and research team members is due to the fact that the ratings made by residents are considerably more reliable than ratings made by members of the research team. The findings fit in with what we know about rating methods generally. The reliability and validity of ratings depend on three things: (1) the *ability* of the rater; (2) the *kind of information* the rater has about the subject; and (3) the *amount of information* the rater has about the subject. Of the three considerations, the first is usually the least important. That is, better ratings are usually obtained from an "ordinary person" who has a considerable amount of experience with the subject than from a highly competent person who has relatively short and narrow acquaintance with the subject. For example, it has been found that sailors do a better job of rating one another than their officers do.

The higher reliability found for residents than for members of the research team is probably due to the fact that the former have more experience with the particular patient-subjects and in more "natural" circumstances of daily contact. The primary reason for the present reliability study was to insure that the ratings made by residents are reliable, and they are. It is their ratings which will be used in correlational and other studies to follow. However, we cannot deny the fact that, whatever the reasons may be, a blow to the pride of the investigators was struck, but at least this has been a worthwhile by-product of the research.

We examined specifically three original protocols of patients who were most highly correlated and three of patients who were least highly correlated, hoping to get some clues. We did find explanations for some of the discrepancy in these specific cases, but nothing of general applicability. In one case the research member apparently responded directly to and recorded correctly a severe, hopeless depression, covered over defensively by an elated optimism that the resident (more accurately in terms of observing what the patient showed at that moment) described. In another case, however, in rechecking the hospital records, nurses' notes, occupational therapy notes, and resident's work-up, it was difficult to believe that the research member had seen the same patient.

Another possibility raised was that perhaps there would be some discrepancies in correlations of stereotypes because of differences in age and experience between the residents and the psychiatrists, so that correlations were broken down into first-, second-, and third-year residents, junior psychiatrists, and senior psychiatrists. These showed only a vague suggestion that the senior psychiatrists rated closer to the residents than did the younger research group, but the results do not have statistical validity. The average intercorrelation *within* each group is as follows:

First-year residents	.52
Second-year residents	.52
Third-year residents	.57
Research team Group I	.72
Research team Group II	.63

The last coefficient shown, .63, is not really an average but a single correlation, that between Psychiatrists D and E. The results show that research team members agree more highly with one another about the "typical" depression than residents do among themselves. The average correlation over all three groups of residents is .53. The average over all for research team members is .70. The difference is substantial and indicates that continued experience and training results in more agreement among psychiatrists about the "typical" depression. Paraphrasing this, one could state that the younger men are more open to the actual data from the patient; the older men are more rigidly bound to their averaged experiences.

As a last resort, an analysis of specific traits was made to see which items the residents and research team agreed about most and disagreed about most. Aside from a clustering of "anxiety" traits as most disagreed upon, the rest of the characteristics seem pretty well spread out. The complete item analysis is included in Table 32.

INFLUENCE OF STEREOTYPES ON RELIABILITY OF RATINGS

A question that was raised in the early stage of the depression research was: to what extent are the psychiatric ratings of individual patients influenced by *stereotypes* of the "typical" depression? The question is important in the current research because it may be that psychiatrists sometimes look *too* hard for *typical* symptoms and end up by seeing them whether they are present or not. This would, of course, constitute a source of error in psychiatric observations, ratings, and diagnoses. Consequently, it is important to find out whether there are stereotypes held by psychiatrists and, if so, to determine the influence of the stereotypes on psychiatrists' decisions.

A small study of stereotypes was undertaken in the early phases of the depression research, the results of which are described in Chapter 5. In that procedure seven psychiatrists made Q-sort ratings of "the typical depression." Separate ratings were made with the feelings and concerns and the current behavior trait lists. The analysis to be described here was designed to enlarge on the earlier findings regarding feelings and concern stereotypes; current behavior stereotypes will be discussed later.

There are several ways in which the present investigation of feelings and concerns stereotypes differed from the earlier one. In the earlier study all 7 psychiatrists were members of the research team. The present one uses 5 psychiatrists from the research team and 16 resident psychiatrists. The earlier study was made with 111 "feelings and concerns" traits; the present with only 47 of those traits.

Twenty-one psychiatrists each rated the "typical depressive case" with the 47-item "feelings and concerns" check list. All intercorrelations were computed for the 21 "stereotypes," resulting in a matrix of 210 coefficients. This showed, for example, that the stereotype held by First-Year Resident III correlates .61 with the stereotype held by Psychiatrist A, and the stereotype held by First-Year Resident V correlates .59 with the stereotype held by Second-Year Resident VIII.

Subsequent to obtaining the correlation matrix, a "principal components" factor analysis was performed. The results were rotated a number of times to achieve a statistically neat solution. The results are reported in Table 33. Factor scores were then determined for each trait on each factor. The results are reported in Tables 34, 35, and 36. Finally, various auxiliary statistics and significant tests were computed in order to further clarify the results.

The principal results of the present study are very similar to those reported in the earlier study. The average correlation in the matrix is .56, which is in the neighborhood of the average correlation of .67 found in the previous study. The high average correlation indicates that there is considerable agreement among psychiatrists as to what the "typical" depressive case is like.

After finding that there is a strong tendency to agree about the stereotype, the next consideration is to determine whether there are systematic disagreements among groups of psychiatrists. This should be answered by the factor-analytic results. Although a factor analysis of feelings and concerns stereotypes was not made in the earlier study, the size and homogeneity of the correlations led to the conclusion that only one important factor was present. The results of the present study lead to much the same conclusion. There is one very strong factor in the correlations (Factor A in Table 33). It proved difficult to find any other factors where more than one or two psychiatrists had high loadings. We finally arrived at Factors B and C as the best that could be done.

Factor A is the "garden variety" depressive as seen by the 21 psychiatrists. Loadings on the factor are generally very high; only one loading is below .60, and nine psychiatrists have loadings of .80 or above. (The trait array for the factor is shown in Table 34). The research team members as a group have significantly more of Factor A than the residents as a group. The difference is significant beyond the .001 level by the "sums of ranks" test. This difference might escape the eye because some of the residents have very high loadings of Factor A. However, all of the relatively low loadings are held by residents, and, consequently, the average for research team members is significantly higher.

Both Factors B and C are bipolar. That is, there are some moderate-sized positive loadings and some moderate-sized negative loadings. If a psychiatrist has a positive loading, it means that he regards the "typical depressive" as being like the trait array for the particular factor. If he has a negative loading, he regards the "typical depressive" as being like the opposite of the trait array. In other words, for a negative loading, the high-ranking traits in the array would be ranked low, and vice versa.

On Factor B only three loadings are above .40. These are the loadings of .62, .41, and −.42 by Residents I, II, and IX respectively. None of the other psychiatrists has loadings large enough to interpret. The average difference between research team members and residents on Factor B is *not* significant.

Factor C is "weaker" than Factor B. Only one loading is above .40. In order to interpret the factor at all, it is necessary to drop the standard to .30, which is risky because only 47 traits were used in the analysis. There are only three psychiatrists who have loadings of .30 or higher. These are .35, .31, and .52, for Residents XII, XV, and IV respectively. The factor does *not* significantly differentiate residents from research team members.

There is undoubtedly a firm stereotype of the "typical depression" held by the psychiatrists participating in this study. Either there is a real "garden variety" depressive which is often met in psychiatric practice, or psychiatrists at least think there is. The trait array for Factor A should provide a useful means of communicating the "garden variety" to others.

In addition to the implications of the results of this study for psychiatric stereotypes, these results also concern the reliability studies performed previously. One possible meaning of the low correlations between the ratings by residents and by research team members was that the rating task simply would not permit high correlations. However, in the study of stereotypes it is found that psychiatrists *can* produce high correlations with the feelings and concerns check list. Consequently, this suggests that the low correlations found in the reliability study were not due to the rating task per se but to a lack of agreement about the characteristics of particular patients.

SUMMARY

Reliability of the feelings and concerns check list by psychiatric residents is on the average high as contrasted with that of members of the research team, whose reliability was discouragingly low. The research psychiatrists with continued training and experience agree more among themselves about the "typical" depression than do the residents. Perhaps this means that the older men are more rigid and the younger ones are more open to the actual data of the individual live patient. Again as in the stereotypes elicited in the pilot study, only one single factor seemed to be important. This is A of the pilot study and I of the full study; in other words, the sad, hopeless, self-castigating person with low self-esteem and some guilt feelings. This means that the presence of the other factors cannot be explained on the basis of pre-existing bias.

TABLE 32

AGREEMENT INDICES FOR THE 47 FEELINGS AND CONCERNS ITEMS USED IN THE RELIABILITY COMPARISON OF RESEARCH TEAM-MEMBERS AND RESIDENTS

Rank	Disagreement Index	Traits
1	0.1	Concern over increasing sexual interest
2	0.3	Increased sexual feelings and interests
3	0.4	Has ideas of committing suicide
4	0.6	Feels he (she) is being persecuted
5	0.6	Feels envious of others
6	0.6	Credits illness to excessive family and/ or job responsibilities
7	0.6	Anger that is present attached to unreasonable object
8	0.7	Considers self lazy
9	0.7	Experiences moodiness
10	0.7	Shame is experienced
11	0.7	Concerned with making up for wrongs to others
12	0.8	Concerned with suffering caused to others
13	0.8	Feels a failure
14	0.8	Feels that the illness was precipitated by recent events
15	0.8	Feels helpless and powerless
16	0.8	Feels optimistic
17	0.8	Feels self unworthy
18	0.8	Feels relieved after hospitalization
19	0.8	Feels that illness would be relieved by the solving of certain "material" problems—money, job, housing, etc.

(Continued)

TABLE 32 *(Continued)*

Rank	Disagreement Index	Traits
20	0.8	Feels ambivalent toward important personal issues
21	0.8	Feels lonely
22	0.8	Professes to have little or no feelings
23	0.9	Has feelings of tenseness
24	0.9	Feels he (she) brought illness on self
25	0.9	Guilt feelings experienced
26	0.9	Feels unloved
27	0.9	Feels hopeful about getting better
28	0.9	Concerned with aging and lessening vigor
29	0.9	Feels hopeless
30	0.9	Gets much secondary gain from illness
31	0.9	Feels loss of esteem by others
32	0.9	Can laugh at times
33	0.9	Feels guilt for not assuming family and/or job responsibilities
34	0.9	Wants to cry much of the time
35	1.0	Experiences free anxiety
36	1.0	Expresses much concern for the welfare of family and friends
37	1.0	Feels burdened by the demands of others
38	1.0	Feelings are dominated by sadness and "blueness"
39	1.0	Feels that he (she) is being brave in bearing troubles
40	1.0	Concerned with material loss—money, property, etc.
41	1.0	Feels "at end of rope"
42	1.1	Has anxiety about particular concerns

(Continued)

TABLE 32 *(Continued)*

Rank	Disagreement Index	Traits
43	1.2	Feels unable to make decisions
44	1.2	Feels "jittery"
45	1.3	Feels unable to act
46	1.3	Feels constantly fatigued
47	1.3	Feels loss of interest in "oral satisfaction"—food, drink, smoking

TABLE 33

ROTATED FACTOR LOADINGS FOR THE STEREOTYPES IN THE FEELINGS AND CONCERNS CHECK LIST

Psychiatrist	Loadings		
	Factor A	Factor B	Factor C
I	.56	.62	-.15
VII	.80	.19	-.19
VIII	.66	-.18	.10
II	.75	.41	.16
XII	.61	.06	-.35
XIII	.85	-.07	-.05
XIV	.72	.10	.23
XV	.78	-.11	-.31
IX	.66	-.42	-.06
X	.72	.08	-.03
III	.79	-.02	-.04
XVI	.81	.02	-.05
IV	.60	-.08	.52
V	.89	-.02	-.20
XI	.86	.01	-.05
VI	.73	-.12	.22
D	.83	-.08	-.09
E	.78	-.10	-.10
A	.80	-.12	.03
B	.80	-.10	.33
C	.84	.02	.15

TABLE 34

ARRAY FOR STEREOTYPE FACTOR A
(HIGHEST AND LOWEST 15 ITEMS)

(The most characteristic item is ranked 1,
the least characteristic is ranked 47)

Rank	Item Title	Item Number
1	Feels hopeless	1
2	Feels self unworthy	10
3	Feels unable to make decisions	32
4	Feels a failure	25
5	Feels helpless and powerless	4
6	Feelings are dominated by sadness and "blueness"	9
7	Feels "at end of rope"	20
8	Feels loss of interest in "oral satisfactions" —food, drink, smoking	13
9	Feels lonely	46
10	Feels unable to act	43
11	Feels constantly fatigued	19
12	Guilt feelings experienced	31
13	Feels loss of esteem by others	34
14	Feels ambivalent toward important personal issues	45
15	Concerned with suffering caused to others	7
33	Considers self lazy	11
34	Anger that is present attached to unreasonable object	30
35	Feels relieved after hospitalization	42
36	Experiences free anxiety	23
37	Credits illness to excessive family and/or job responsibility	47

(Continued)

TABLE 34 *(Continued)*

Rank	Item Title	Item Number
38	Feels envious of others	22
39	Professes to have little or no feelings	39
40	Feels that illness would be relieved by the solving of certain "material" problems—money, job, housing, etc.	8
41	Feels he (she) is being persecuted	6
42	Can laugh at times	3
43	Feels that he (she) is being brave in bearing troubles	2
44	Feels hopeful about getting better	24
45	Concern over increasing sexual interest	40
46	Feels optimistic	12
47	Increased sexual feelings and interests	18

TABLE 35

ARRAY FOR STEREOTYPE FACTOR B
(Highest and Lowest 10 Items)

(The most characteristic item is ranked 1,
the least characteristic is ranked 47)

Rank	Item Title	Item Number
1	Has anxiety about particular concerns	33
2	Feels "jittery"	41
3	Feels constantly fatigued	19
4	Professes to have little or no feelings	39
5	Feels helpless and powerless	4
6	Experiences moodiness	37
7	Feels that illness would be relieved by the solving of certain "material" problems—money, job, housing, etc.	8
8	Experiences free anxiety	23
9	Concerned with aging and lessening vigor	26
10	Feels relieved after hospitalization	42
38	Anger that is present attached to unreasonable object	30
39	Feels ambivalent toward important personal issues	45
40	Has ideas of committing suicide	16
41	Gets much secondary gain from illness	28
42	Feels he (she) is being persecuted	6
43	Shame is experienced	44
44	Feels unloved	36
45	Feels loss of esteem by others	34
46	Feels he (she) brought illness on self	15
47	Concerned with suffering caused to others	7

TABLE 36

ARRAY FOR STEREOTYPE FACTOR C
(Highest and Lowest 10 Items)

Rank	Item Title	Item Number
1	Feels unable to act	43
2	Feels relieved after hospitalization	42
3	Feels a failure	25
4	Feels constantly fatigued	19
5	Feels burdened by the demands of others	38
6	Feels that he (she) is being brave in bearing troubles	2
7	Feelings are dominated by sadness and "blueness"	9
8	Feels unloved	36
9	Feels hopeless	1
10	Increased sexual feelings and interests	18
38	Experiences free anxiety	23
39	Shame is experienced	44
40	Concerned with material loss—money, property, etc.	17
41	Feels that illness would be relieved by the solving of certain "material" problems—money, job, housing, etc.	8
42	Feels "jittery"	41
43	Anger that is present attached to unreasonable object	30
44	Has feelings of tenseness	5
45	Guilt feelings experienced	31
46	Has anxiety about particular concerns	33
47	Concerned with making up for wrongs to others	27

~~~~~~~~~~~~~~~~~~~~~~~~~~~~~~~~~~

CHAPTER 9

Factor Analysis of Current Behavior Check List

IN THE BEGINNING STAGES OF OUR RESEARCH, A distinction was made between feelings and concerns traits and current behavior traits. The first study consisted of having psychiatrists rate 21 cases with a Q-sort of feelings and concerns items and with a Q-sort of current behavior items. Analysis of the former produced three factors; no factor analysis was performed with the latter. Subsequently, both groups of traits were expanded and used in a larger study in which, instead of using the Q-sort, conventional rating scales were employed. A factor analysis was performed on the feelings and concerns traits for the 96 patients, and five factors were obtained. The next step in the analysis was to factor-analyze the current behavior traits and compare the results with those obtained from the feelings and concerns items.

STATISTICAL METHOD USED IN ANALYZING THE DATA

Each item on the current behavior form is rated dichotomously; that is, it either appears in the patient or does not appear. One of the first important pieces of information to obtain is the frequency of occurrence of each item, for two reasons. First, it reveals those traits that seldom appear in depressed patients.

Second, it indicates those traits which cannot contribute prominently to factor-analytic results. If a trait almost always occurs or almost never occurs, it cannot correlate highly with other traits and, consequently, will not add to factor-analytic results. Because the total number of items is so large (139) that a factor analysis would strain even a digital computer, it was important to shorten the list of traits to those that might contribute to the analysis. Consequently, traits that occurred more than 90 per cent of the time or occurred less than 10 per cent of the time were not used in the factor analysis. These items, 47 in all, are marked by an asterisk in Table 37. In addition there were very little data on eight other items concerned with occupational therapy, so that they could not be included.

The ratings of the 96 patients on the 84 items were intercorrelated, resulting in a total of 3,486 correlation coefficients. These correlations were subjected to a centroid factor analysis, and 16 factors were extracted which were then rotated by the Varimax method. Four of the resulting factors had loadings too small to be given serious consideration. Two more of the factors turned out to be mainly "couplets"; only two items had high loadings which were artificially related in content. This left ten potentially useful factors, all of which appear to have sufficient statistical strength, i.e., enough items on each factor and sufficiently high loadings.

The factor lists below contain only those items that are most characteristic of each factor. A positive loading means that the item is characteristic of the factor, and a negative loading means that the item is the opposite of the factor. The full set of loadings of all items on all ten factors is given in Table 38.

INTERPRETATION OF THE FACTORS ELICITED

We now turn to the ten "current behavior" factors and attempt to determine whether they have clinical meaning.

Factor 1

Loading	Item No.	
+.72	109	Isolated and withdrawn
+.59	110	Prefers to remain by him(her)self
+.43	76	Stays in bed much of the time
−.55	2	Complains of boredom
−.56	125	Communicates with men
−.64	118	Becomes part of a small clique
−.68	103	Communicates with other patients
−.75	108	Enters into activity with group on unit

Factor I describes the obviously isolated, withdrawn patient who behaves in accordance with a feeling of deep depression. Described among the negative traits are those dealing with communication and participation in group activities.

Factor 2

Loading	Item No.	
+.69	88	Speech slurred and mumbled
+.61	89	Speech slowed and retarded
+.58	41	Thought processes slow and retarded
+.46	80	Has flat, masklike face
−.43	123	Seems alert and responsive
−.56	101	Communicates easily and well
−.66	100	Pays attention to grooming
−.69	98	Clean and neat

The items characteristic of Factor 2 are slowing and retardation of both speech and thought and the depressed masklike facies. These patients are not alert or communicative nor are they attentive to good grooming, neatness, or cleanliness.

Factor 3

Loading	Item No.	
+.60	72	Gait and general behavior slow and retarded
+.59	87	Volume of voice decreased
+.50	75	Sits alone very quietly
+.48	58	Shows little or no interest in opposite sex
−.46	10	Complains of having been provoked or of becoming angry
−.53	23	Witty and charming
−.55	25	Unconvincing gaiety
−.69	8	Reports feeling cheerful

Factor 3 includes retardation, withdrawal, loss of interest, and aloofness. The picture is not so much the deep depression of Factor 1 but more loss of interest and apathy.

Factor 4

Loading	Item No.	
+.70	113	Complains constantly about hospital, staff, food, etc.
+.64	18	Provokes anger in staff or patients
+.61	104	Makes excessive demands
+.48	90	Speech rapid and accelerated
+.46	128	Response to similar situation varies
−.45	115	Expresses appreciation for care and interest of staff
−.61	114	Seems pleased by facilities and care in hospital

Traits in Factor 4 characterize the unappreciative, actively angry, and provocative patient who makes excessive demands and complaints.

Factor 5

Loading	Item No.	
+.60	97	Dizzy spells
+.58	49	Is constipated (since onset of illness)
+.56	107	Complains frequently of somatic symptoms
+.48	94	Complains of troubles with eyes
+.47	95	Especially sensitive to noise
+.45	12	Complains of being suspicious of staff or other patients
+.44	81	Picks at self or clothing

In Factor 5 are the hypochondriacal, somewhat suspicious patients who have no somatic disturbances but only complaints. They insist that their troubles are due to organic disease and have or gain little insight into the delusionary basis of their complaints.

Factor 6

Loading	Item No.	
+.80	33	Impairment of recent memory
+.71	34	Impairment of remote memory
+.67	37	States he (she) is confused
+.56	38	Cannot concentrate
+.40	42	Limited and repetitive thought content
−.75	32	Memory is good

Factor 6 describes profound cognitive disturbances which give the picture of an organic brain disease, from which they are with difficulty differentiated, especially when the patients are advanced in years. These cognitive symptoms are not due to drugs or shock treatment since our ratings were made before somatotherapy was instituted.

Factor 7

Loading	Item No.	
+.73	13	Complains of being anxious
+.63	129	Expresses need for help
+.62	130	Approaches other people as a source of help
+.60	86	Tremulous
+.47	14	Overtly anxious (shows any of these: widened palpebral fissure, dilated pupils, moist palms, tremor, tense facial musculature)
+.47	1	Complains of being sad and "blue"

Factor 7 is the agitated factor composed of persons who are more apprehensive, tremulous, and overtly anxious than depressed although that mood is also present.

Factor 8

Loading	Item No.	
+.51	83	Holds self stiff and rigid
+.43	80	Has flat, masklike face
−.40	5	Restless (has difficulty in remaining still)
−.48	93	Has headaches
−.54	126	Communicates with women
−.63	102	Communicates with staff

Factor 8 is the immobile, rigid person who suggests the Parkinsonian syndrome or the effect of a long period of administration of some of the tranquilizing drugs. However, these drugs had, to our knowledge, not been prescribed.

Factor 9

Loading	Item No.	
+.60	59	Has excessively dry skin
+.59	60	Has dry hair and scalp; difficulty in combing hair
+.52	79	Changes tasks frequently
+.47	94	Complains of troubles with eyes
−.43	139	Physical examination is essentially negative

Dominating in Factor 9 are symptoms of definite somatic disturbances, not hypochondriasis. These symptoms are characteristic of the dry depression. They are mild symptoms and are short-lasting. This does not confirm the hypothesis of Schmale (1958). In a study of the relationship of depression to the onset of somatic diseases of all types, he concluded that the dynamics of depression (actual, threatened, or symbolic loss of a love-object) are antecedent to the precipitation of a wide range of diseases.

Factor 10

Loading	Item No.	
+.67	122	Tries to "do good" for other patients and to help the staff with their work
+.66	121	Acts ingratiatingly with staff
+.50	115	Expresses appreciation for care and interest of staff
+.43	114	Seems pleased by facilities and care in the hospital

Factor 10 characterizes the clinging patient who ingratiatingly pleads for love and desperately attempts to win approval.

FACTOR-ANALYTIC RESULTS

Table 39 shows the mean factor scores for four groups of patients on each of the ten factors, which should serve as guides to interpreting the factor scores of individual patients. Thus, if on Factor 1 a patient has a factor score greater than .45, he has more than average. Conversely, if the factor score is less than .45, the patient has less than average of the factor.

Turning now to the differentiation between the 96 depression cases and those in the other three small groups, we see that the differences are less prominent than in "feelings and concerns" (compare with Table 33). Factor 3 in behavior, which is the apathetic, indifferent group, seems most characteristic of the D-D group as well as the O-D group, which also ultimately turned out to warrant a diagnosis of depression. On the other hand, the D-O group showed few somatic symptoms and little evidence of cognitive disturbances. Factor 7, composed of items characterizing agitation, seemed to be lowest in the O-O group, indicating again the weight of agitation or anxiety in making the diagnosis of depression.

SUMMARY

The factor analysis of current behavior ratings elicited ten factors which correspond well with clinical descriptions based on empirical observations. These may be epitomized by single phrases as follows:

1. The isolated and withdrawn
2. The slowed and retarded in speech and thought
3. The disinterested and apathetic
4. The angrily provocative and demanding
5. The hypochondriacal
6. The cognitively disturbed (questionable organic brain changes)
7. The agitated
8. The rigid, immobile
9. The somatically disturbed
10. The clinging, ingratiatingly pleading for love and attention

Behavioral differentiation of the admitted-as-depressed-discharged-as-depressed group from the others was much less than by feelings and concerns. The all-the-way-depressed were highest in apathy as well as were those in the admitted-as-other-discharged-as-depressed. The admitted-depressed-discharged-other showed little separate characterization. Those never considered depressed were lowest in agitation (Factor 7).

TABLE 37

PERCENTAGE OF OCCURRENCE OF EACH ITEM IN THE 96 PATIENTS
(*Indicates that percentage of occurrence was either too large or too
small to permit the item to be used in the factor analysis)

Trait	Per Cent Possessing Trait
1. Complains of being sad and blue	48
2. Complains of boredom	37
3. Cries (lacrimation)	37
4. Sobs (no lacrimation)	10
5. Restless (has difficulty in remaining still)	78
* 6. Never smiles	6
* 7. Seen to smile at some time during observation	97
8. Reports feeling cheerful	14
* 9. Destroys objects or strikes at people	1
10. Complains of having been provoked or of becoming angry	20
* 11. Shouts, raises voice, or uses derogatory language	8
12. Complains of being suspicious of staff or other patients	14
13. Complains of being anxious	59
14. Overtly anxious (shows any of these: widened palpebral fissure, dilated pupils, moist palms, tremor, tense facial musculature)	67
* 15. Complains of being unable to cry	4
16. Shows evidence of humor (responds appropriately to humorous situations and/or can make other people laugh)	81
17. Composed	66
18. Provokes anger in staff or patients	10

(Continued)

TABLE 37 *(Continued)*

Trait	Per Cent Possessing Trait
* 19. Flirtatious	7
* 20. Shows off body or possessions	4
* 21. Appears in lounge in state of undress	7
* 22. Wide fluctuations and variability in behavior	7
23. Witty and charming	15
* 24. Wide and rapid mood changes	6
25. Unconvincing gaiety	28
* 26. Well oriented for time, place, and person	93
* 27. Has obvious hallucinations	0
* 28. Has obvious delusions	5
* 29. States the environment is not real	2
* 30. States that he (she) feels unreal	6
* 31. Misidentifies people	7
32. Memory is good	76
33. Impairment of recent memory	21
34. Impairment of remote memory	14
* 35. Acts as though he (she) understands what is said to him (her)	97
* 36. Acts as though he (she) understands the hospital environment	93
37. States he (she) is confused	21
38. Cannot concentrate	57
* 39. Talks of strange and unusual ideas or fantasies	5
* 40. Has distorted sense of time	6
41. Thought processes are slow and retarded	46
42. Limited and repetitive thought content	42
43. Appetite poor	55

(Continued)

177

TABLE 37 *(Continued)*

Trait	Per Cent Possessing Trait
* 44. Increased appetite	4
* 45. Craving for special foods	6
46. Nauseated	13
* 47. Vomits	4
* 48. Has diarrhea (since onset of illness)	4
49. Is constipated (since onset of illness)	27
50. Shows bloating and belching	10
* 51. Eats with group in lounge	92
* 52. Eats at frequent intervals between meals	3
* 53. Eats breakfast	98
* 54. Eats lunch	99
* 55. Eats dinner	99
* 56. Eats alone in room	8
* 57. Shows marked interest in opposite sex	3
58. Shows little or no interest in opposite sex	69
59. Has excessively dry skin	17
60. Has dry hair and scalp; difficulty in combing hair	16
* 61. Recent change in skin color	8
* 62. Change in hair color	0
63. Sweating increased	19
* 64. Sweating decreased	2
* 65. Has specific skin lesions or eruptions	0
66. Difficulty in getting to sleep	55
67. Wakefulness during the night	35
68. Wakes very early in the morning	47

(Continued)

TABLE 37 *(Continued)*

Trait	Per Cent Possessing Trait
69. Required sedation for sleep after the first 48 hours of hospitalization	87
70. Sleeps during the day	21
* 71. Sleeps excessively	2
72. Gait and general behavior slow and retarded	58
73. Paces floor	49
74. Wrings hands	28
75. Sits alone very quietly	71
76. Stays in bed much of the time	20
* 77. Constantly active	8
* 78. Assumes unusual postures	1
79. Changes tasks frequently	13
80. Has flat, masklike face	51
81. Picks at self or clothing	13
* 82. Is dramatic and theatrical	7
83. Holds self stiff and rigid	26
* 84. Has ticlike movements	3
85. Is easily distractable	01
86. Tremulous	42
87. Volume of voice decreased	57
88. Speech slurred and mumbled	19
89. Speech slowed and retarded	33
90. Speech rapid and accelerated	10
* 91. Speech stilted and artificial	6
92. Sighs	79
93. Has headaches	55

(Continued)

TABLE 37 *(Continued)*

Trait	Per Cent Possessing Trait
94. Complains of troubles with eyes	13
95. Especially sensitive to noise	19
* 96. Has bad taste in mouth	4
97. Dizzy spells	23
98. Clean and neat	85
* 99. Dresses appropriately	98
100. Pays attention to grooming	74
101. Communicates easily and well	42
102. Communicates with staff	88
103. Communicates with other patients	71
104. Makes excessive demands	12
105. Clinging	27
106. Requests center around medication or physical treatments	29
107. Complains frequently of somatic symptoms	30
108. Enters into activity with group on unit	52
109. Isolated and withdrawn	33
110. Prefers to remain by him(her)self	54
* 111. Becomes a leader in unit activities	5
112. Follows others' suggestions passively ("goes along")	71
113. Complains constantly about hospital, staff, food, etc.	10
114. Seems pleased by facilities and care in the hospital	54
115. Expresses apppreciation for care and interest of staff	54
* 116. Is disruptive of group activities	1

(Continued)

TABLE 37 *(Continued)*

Trait	Per Cent Possessing Trait
* 117. Disruptive of staff attention to other patients	5
118. Becomes part of a small clique	32
119. Feels more comfortable after hospitalization	82
120. Feels less comfortable after hospitalization	13
121. Acts ingratiatingly with staff	33
122. Tries to "do good" for other patients and to help the staff with their work	21
123. Seems alert and responsive	65
124. Relates in a distant and guarded manner	59
125. Communicates with men	58
126. Communicates with women	89
* 127. Evidence of suicidal thoughts or behavior	6
128. Response to similar situation varies	10
129. Expresses need for help	56
130. Approaches other people as a source of help	47
†	
139. Physical examination is essentially negative	67

† Items 131-138 were omitted because of incomplete data.

TABLE 38

FACTOR LOADINGS FOR ALL ITEMS ON ALL 10 CURRENT BEHAVIOR FACTORS

Item	Factor									
	1	2	3	4	5	6	7	8	9	10
1. Complains of being sad and blue	.07	-.07	.07	.03	.11	.08	.47	.09	.10	-.01
2. Complains of boredom	-.55	.03	.01	.11	.09	.08	-.08	-.12	.07	-.12
3. Cries (lacrimation)	.06	-.15	.10	-.07	.16	.11	.18	-.05	-.08	-.07
4. Sobs (no lacrimation)	.28	.06	.02	.30	.37	.07	.08	-.01	.01	.11
5. Restless (has difficulty in remaining still)	-.12	.10	.20	.21	-.02	.32	.27	-.40	-.08	-.02
8. Reports feeling cheerful	-.15	-.13	-.69	.01	-.14	-.13	.02	-.04	-.14	.00
10. Complains of having been provoked or of becoming angry	-.21	.05	-.46	.39	.06	-.10	-.07	-.17	.17	-.14
12. Complains of being suspicious of staff or other patients	.06	.18	-.39	.08	.45	.08	.18	.09	-.01	-.21
13. Complains of being anxious	.06	.06	-.10	.06	.04	.00	.73	-.04	.10	.22
14. Overtly anxious (shows any of these: widened palpebral fissure, dilated pupils, moist palms, tremor, tense facial musculature)	.11	.27	.06	-.02	-.03	.09	.47	-.22	.02	-.10
16. Shows evidence of humor (responds appropriately to humorous situations and/or can make other people laugh)	-.29	-.09	-.11	-.30	-.12	-.18	-.26	-.14	-.01	.19
17. Composed	-.30	-.28	.02	-.22	-.08	-.34	-.20	.06	-.16	.10

18. Provokes anger in staff or patients	-.02	.10	-.13	.64	.16	.10	-.08	-.02	.01	-.04
23. Witty and charming	-.26	-.28	-.53	-.15	-.17	.08	.11	-.10	.00	-.02
25. Unconvincing gaiety	-.29	-.09	-.55	-.01	-.15	.07	.04	-.17	-.15	.18
32. Memory is good	-.14	-.21	-.10	-.23	-.08	-.75	-.02	-.20	-.10	.06
33. Impairment of recent memory	.06	.14	.05	.14	-.01	.80	-.07	.09	.17	-.08
34. Impairment of remote memory	.08	.30	-.07	-.01	.04	.71	.00	.03	.14	.00
37. States he (she) is confused	.04	.05	-.01	.00	.01	.67	.21	-.01	-.04	-.08
38. Cannot concentrate	.05	.04	.04	-.05	.16	.56	.11	.02	.10	-.06
41. Thought processes are slow and retarded	.14	.58	.19	-.11	.04	.35	.05	.25	-.04	.10
42. Limited and repetitive thought content	.20	.07	.34	-.02	.05	.40	.09	-.13	.19	.04
43. Appetite poor	.39	.03	-.03	-.06	.10	.10	.02	-.06	.10	-.07
46. Nauseated	-.09	-.12	.17	.30	.33	-.25	.14	-.22	.04	-.08
49. Is constipated (since onset of illness)	-.12	.18	.05	-.10	.58	.11	.08	-.01	-.05	-.01
50. Shows bloating and belching	-.20	-.02	.05	.27	.27	.02	.32	-.12	.04	-.16
58. Shows little or no interest in opposite sex	.15	.28	.48	.15	.21	.06	.14	-.18	-.02	.10
59. Has excessively dry skin	.15	.15	.07	.08	-.03	.36	-.04	.12	.60	-.03
60. Has dry hair and scalp; difficulty in combing hair	.01	.23	.08	.25	.14	.10	.02	.10	.59	.04
63. Sweating increased	-.05	.24	-.03	.12	-.05	.15	.15	-.16	.06	.06
66. Difficulty in getting to sleep	.09	.08	.10	-.04	.16	.02	.03	-.09	-.10	.01
67. Wakefulness during the night	.15	.02	.10	.35	.12	-.03	-.08	-.06	-.08	-.10

(Continued)

TABLE 38 (Continued)

Item	Factor									
	1	2	3	4	5	6	7	8	9	10
68. Wakes very early in the morning	-.18	.13	.04	.05	.06	.16	.07	-.01	.03	.00
69. Required sedation for sleep after the first 48 hours of hospitalization	.05	.02	.03	-.03	.04	-.05	.07	.10	.05	.11
70. Sleeps during the day	.17	.25	-.01	.25	.06	-.20	.39	-.15	-.04	-.16
72. Gait and general behavior slow and retarded	.12	.32	.60	-.11	-.03	.18	-.10	.13	-.21	-.22
73. Paces floor	.23	.35	.08	.07	-.13	.39	.13	-.19	.00	.21
74. Wrings hands	.39	.03	.25	.07	.02	.18	.23	-.04	.23	.15
75. Sits alone very quietly	.29	-.09	.50	-.01	-.31	-.10	.08	.09	.00	-.37
76. Stays in bed much of the time	.43	-.02	.02	-.03	.39	-.05	-.16	.16	.05	-.14
79. Changes tasks frequently	-.15	-.06	-.27	.30	-.07	.10	.04	.02	.52	.17
80. Has flat, masklike face	.28	.46	.33	.03	-.06	.04	-.18	.43	.06	-.15
81. Picks at self or clothing	.35	.24	.00	.18	.44	.18	.18	.00	.17	.06
83. Holds self stiff and rigid	-.02	.03	.16	.07	.04	.26	.03	.51	.04	.01
85. Is easily distractable	-.19	.16	-.12	.39	.10	.21	.11	-.20	.06	.06
86. Tremulous	.12	.05	.15	.05	.00	.18	.60	.07	.11	-.12
87. Volume of voice decreased	.00	.26	.59	-.25	-.07	.10	.10	-.02	-.07	-.32
88. Speech slurred and mumbled	.09	.69	.10	-.16	.08	.16	.11	.03	.02	-.14
89. Speech slowed and retarded	.22	.61	.27	-.21	-.01	.19	.03	.05	-.09	-.21

90. Speech rapid and accelerated	.19	-.07	-.29	.48	-.04	.10	.14	-.04	.14	-.01
92. Sighs	.05	-.03	.17	-.06	.13	.37	.07	-.15	.24	-.01
93. Has headaches	-.01	.07	.05	.10	.18	.29	.07	-.48	-.10	-.12
94. Complains of troubles with eyes	.06	.11	-.04	.04	.48	.14	.05	.05	.47	.13
95. Especially sensitive to noise	-.05	.01	.14	.33	.47	-.05	.24	-.05	.04	.04
97. Dizzy spells	.12	-.06	.10	.25	.60	.05	.31	-.03	.02	.02
98. Clean and neat	.07	-.69	-.04	-.09	-.04	-.01	-.05	.11	-.27	-.02
100. Pays attention to grooming	-.07	-.66	-.06	-.10	-.10	-.22	.08	-.04	-.29	.06
101. Communicates easily and well	-.24	-.56	-.33	-.06	-.05	-.13	.07	-.24	.09	.01
102. Communicates with staff	-.17	-.15	-.12	.00	.24	-.09	.07	-.63	.02	.04
103. Communicates with other patients	-.68	-.18	-.10	.00	.02	-.16	-.03	-.17	-.13	.05
104. Makes excessive demands	-.01	-.14	.01	.61	.14	.10	.03	-.13	.13	.19
105. Clinging	.12	.09	-.04	.27	.23	.37	.19	-.01	.01	.35
106. Requests center around medication or physical treatments	.11	-.06	.20	.38	.35	-.04	.14	-.27	.16	.06
107. Complains frequently of somatic symptoms	.14	.06	.20	.39	.56	.02	.04	-.27	-.01	.19
108. Enters into activity with group on unit	-.75	-.02	-.08	-.09	-.11	-.20	.07	-.01	-.07	.29
109. Isolated and withdrawn	.72	.20	.18	-.13	.18	.10	-.13	-.11	.06	-.27
110. Prefers to remain by him(her)self	.59	.14	.27	-.12	-.04	-.06	-.06	-.04	.13	-.37

(Continued)

TABLE 38 (Continued)

Item	Factor									
	1	2	3	4	5	6	7	8	9	10
112. Follows others' suggestions passively ("goes along")	-.04	.05	.17	-.13	-.36	.04	.13	.07	-.20	.13
113. Complains constantly about hospital, staff, food, etc.	-.10	-.09	.08	.70	.23	-.01	.11	.15	.18	.10
114. Seems pleased by facilities and care in the hospital	-.21	-.15	-.09	-.61	-.01	-.18	.12	-.06	.06	.43
115. Expresses appreciation for care and interest of staff	-.24	-.25	-.10	-.45	.13	-.19	.23	-.16	.09	.50
118. Becomes part of a small clique	-.64	-.09	-.15	.01	.01	.01	-.11	-.17	.08	.02
119. Feels more comfortable after hospitalization	-.08	.09	.07	-.25	-.05	-.02	.03	.06	.03	-.07
120. Feels less comfortable after hospitalization	.09	-.03	-.09	.16	.07	.02	.00	-.11	.06	.06
121. Acts ingratiatingly with staff	-.08	-.14	-.11	.12	.15	.03	.13	-.26	-.09	.66
122. Tries to "do good" for other patients and to help the staff with their work	-.23	.04	-.07	-.05	-.09	-.09	.01	.08	.12	.67
123. Seems alert and responsive	-.39	-.43	-.24	-.26	-.03	-.36	-.04	-.12	.04	.10
124. Relates in a distant and guarded manner	.37	.09	.07	.03	.07	-.01	-.17	-.02	-.34	-.27
125. Communicates with men	-.56	-.11	-.31	-.13	-.06	-.26	-.10	.05	.14	-.06
126. Communicates with women	-.04	-.12	-.04	.06	-.15	-.15	.03	-.54	-.06	.19
128. Response to similar situation varies	-.17	-.10	-.07	.46	-.19	.03	.08	.01	.16	.03
129. Expresses need for help	-.02	-.07	.02	-.02	.31	.11	.63	-.26	-.16	.26
130. Approaches other people as a source of help	-.17	-.05	-.17	-.07	.23	.14	.62	-.07	-.09	.12
139. Physical examination is essentially negative	.09	-.15	-.18	-.01	.11	-.17	-.22	.25	-.43	.35

TABLE 39

MEAN CURRENT BEHAVIOR FACTOR SCORES FOR
VARIOUS GROUPS OF PATIENTS

	Admitted Depressive, Discharged Depressive	Admitted Other, Discharged Depressive	Admitted Depressive, Discharged Other	Admitted Other, Discharged Other
Factor 1	.45	.31	.38	.52
Factor 2	.36	.40	.16	.47
Factor 3	.76	.63	.60	.55
Factor 4	.21	.12	.34	.30
Factor 5	.20	.24	.18	.24
Factor 6	.30	.39	.17	.48
Factor 7	.53	.58	.56	.40
Factor 8	.28	.25	.27	.25
Factor 9	.16	.13	.08	.34
Factor 10	.41	.50	.34	.48

CHAPTER 10

Reliability Studies of Current Behavior Ratings

As we have stated in connection with each factor analysis, reliability studies are essential before confidence can be placed in the results of substantive investigations. Reliability studies on current behavior factors are reported in Table 40. The reliability measure used is referred to as "coefficient alpha," which, for the ten factors, ranges from .64 to .86.

DEGREE OF RELIABILITY OBTAINED

Factor scores are obtained by adding ratings of the items which have high loadings on each factor. In adding the items scores, it is assumed that the items within a factor all measure the same thing and to the extent that this is true the factor scores are meaningful. Coefficient alpha indicates the extent to which the items within a factor measure the same attribute; the higher the coefficient the better. Those factors with high coefficients, like Factors 2 and 6, can be trusted more than those with low coefficients, like 8 and 9. Considering that only a relatively small number of items is used for each factor, the reliabilities for the current behavior factors are approximately as good as those found for feelings and concerns factors.

TABLE 40

RELIABILITY OF FACTOR SCORES
FROM CURRENT BEHAVIOR CHECK LIST

Factor Number	Reliability (coefficient alpha*)
1	.83
2	.86
3	.80
4	.75
5	.76
6	.84
7	.75
8	.64
9	.65
10	.74

*See Guilford (1954) for mathematics involved.

The required level of reliability depends on the way in which factor scores are used. If the factors are used in actual clinical diagnosis and treatment, reliabilities would have to be above .85. However, if factor scores are used only in research, as they have been so far, only modest reliability is needed. Even the two factors with the lowest reliability (8 and 9) meet the minimum levels needed for most research purposes.

INFLUENCE OF STEREOTYPES ON RELIABILITY OF RATINGS

One of the goals in the research was to delineate the stereotype of the depressed patient as viewed by psychiatrists and others.

We have already presented a factor analysis of stereotypes as evidenced in the feelings and concerns of depressed patients in Chapter 8. We shall now describe a parallel study conducted with current behavior traits.

The basic data for the study consists of the responses by 16 resident psychiatrists and 9 psychiatric nurses on a check list of 139 traits. Each was asked to mark the check list in such a way as to describe the "typical" depressed patient. Analyses of the data were made to determine the agreed-on stereotype held by the raters as a group and to determine the amounts and kinds of disagreement about particular features.

All possible intercorrelations among the 25 raters were computed, resulting in a matrix of 300 coefficients. The correlation matrix was factored by the centroid method, and eight factors were extracted. After rotating the factors, four appeared to be "strong" enough to study further. The rotated factor loadings are given in Table 41, and the factor arrays are given in Tables 42, 43, 44, and 45 respectively.

Factor A represents the common ground of agreement about the depressed patient in terms of "current behavior" traits. All but three of the raters have loadings above .50 on the factor. On the average, loadings on the factors in this data are somewhat smaller than those found previously in the feelings and concerns data. Even though there is a small difference, the more surprising finding is the absolute strength of the stereotype as shown in Table 41. Because of the diversity of the current behavior traits and because there is little reason for many of the traits to be common to many depressive cases, it was expected to find less agreement about the general stereotype than is evidenced in Factor A. Evidently, the raters agree moderately well about the nature of the "typical depressive," even regarding relatively detailed symptoms.

Because the traits in the current behavior check list are diverse and in many cases "molecular," factor A does not "come alive" as a recognizable type of person. Its array should be regarded mainly as an actuarial table which indicates the expected frequency of occurrence of various symptoms in depressed patients.

Factors B, C, and D are not very strong, so that it is not expected that *all* of the high traits in an array and *all* of the low traits are meaningfully related. With loadings the size of those found on these three factors, the most that can be expected is to find a half-dozen or so high traits and as many low traits which suggest a central theme for a particular factor. It is expected to find considerable "noise" in each factor array, in the sense that some of the high traits and some of the low traits will have no meaningful relation to the central theme.

Because of the relatively low loadings on Factors B, C, and D, only the extremes of each array can be trusted. It is fairly safe to interpret the top and bottom 10 or 15 traits in each array. There may be some traits beyond these limits that appear to be related to the central theme of the factor, but it is doubtful that many traits outside of the top 20 and bottom will be so related.

Factors B, C, and D are bipolar. That is, for each of them some raters have positive loadings and some have negative loadings. For example, Resident XIII has a loading of .40 on Factor B and consequently portrays the typical depressed patient as relatively incommunicative. In contrast, Resident XI has a loading of −.38 on Factor B, which shows that he views the typical depressed patient as relatively communicative. Bipolar Factors C and D are to be interpreted in the same general way.

The examples above for Factor B will help illustrate another point. The loadings represent only "tendencies" and not fixed patterns of response by the raters. For example, looking at the current behavior check list reponses of Resident XIII and Nurse 4, it is seen that the former does not check "yes" on all of the items that indicate communicativeness and the latter does **not** mark all of those items "no." But Resident XIII marks considerably more of the items "yes" than does Nurse 4, and vice versa for the items which indicate lack of communication.

The factor loadings in Table 41 indicate the composition of each person's stereotype. For example, Resident XV emphasizes Factor A and has little of the other three factors. Nurse 5 places little emphasis on A, none on B and D, and emphasizes C strongly.

The factors do not obviously differentiate first-, second-, and third-year residents from one another. On the average, nurses have slightly less of Factor A than do resident psychiatrists. However, this is due entirely to the low loadings by Nurse 5. Factors B, C, and D do not materially differentiate residents from nurses. However, it is interesting that the highest loadings on B and on C are by nurses, and on Factor D a nurse is tied for high loading. However, rather than emphasizing the differences, the results largely indicate that the stereotype held by psychiatric nurses is much the same as that held by resident psychiatrists.

SUMMARY

Reliabilities of the current behavior factors are high although not as good as those found for feelings and concerns. As an added check and for the purpose of determining how professional persons think about depressed patients, 16 psychiatric residents and 9 graduate psychiatric nurses filled out a check list of 139 traits. Four factors were found, of which only A was very strong. It describes patients who have mixtures of symptoms common to several factors of the ten found in the full-scale study of current behavior. In other words, Factor A of the stereotypes, although strong, can be compared only to a list of symptoms in rank order of frequency. Factors B, C, and D are weak, as demonstrated by the low trait loading. Yet their top and bottom 15 traits represent the frequency of symptoms found in depressions of various types. The factors do not differentiate nurses from residents or members of each group from each other. They do, however, reveal that these professional people do not possess a strongly held stereotyped concept of behavior for depressed patients but rather a list of possible behaviors that vary somewhat in rank order.

TABLE 41

ROTATED FACTOR LOADINGS FOR THE STEREOTYPES
IN THE CURRENT BEHAVIOR CHECK LIST

Rater	Factor A	Factor B	Factor C	Factor D
Residents				
I	.45	-.10	-.14	-.45
II	.66	.26	.04	-.17
III	.70	.37	-.19	-.02
IV	.68	.18	.22	.23
V	.69	-.01	.09	.23
VI	.73	.15	.32	.00
VII	.67	.02	.16	.25
VIII	.66	-.25	-.12	.23
IX	.75	.27	-.04	-.17
X	.65	.03	-.32	.08
XI	.56	-.38	-.14	.21
XII	.71	.03	-.35	.05
XIII	.54	.40	-.36	.10
XIV	.66	-.27	.16	-.15
XV	.73	.01	.28	.04
XVI	.65	.10	.09	.36
Nurses				
1	.64	-.38	.07	-.06
2	.56	.41	-.13	.11
3	.68	.05	-.07	-.45
4	.41	-.50	-.15	.26
5	.22	.02	-.56	.02
6	.63	-.29	.32	-.23
7	.70	.21	.16	-.14
8	.65	-.10	.39	-.01
9	.69	-.21	.20	-.20

TABLE 42

ARRAY FOR CURRENT BEHAVIOR STEREOTYPE FACTOR A
(Highest and Lowest 10 Items)

Rank	Item	Item Number
1	Clinging	105
2	Complains frequently of somatic symptoms	107
3	Wakefulness during the night	67
4	Acts as though he (she) understands what is said to him (her).	35
5	Eats dinner	55
6	Cannot concentrate	38
7	Acts as though he (she) understands the hospital environment	36
8	Follows others' suggestions passively (''goes along'').	112
9	Sighs	92
10	Volume of voice decreased	87
11	Well oriented for time, place, and person	26
12	Appetite poor	43
13	Wakes very early in the morning	68
14	Difficulty in starting projects	131
15	Required sedation for sleep after the first 48 hours of hospitalization	69
125	Is disruptive of group activities	116
126	Increased appetite	44
127	Craving for special foods	45
128	Impairment of remote memory	34
129	Misidentifies people	31
130	Becomes a leader in unit activities	111
131	Uses bright vivid colors	138
132	Destroys objects or strikes at people	9

(Continued)

TABLE 42 *(Continued)*

Rank	Item	Item Number
133	Flirtatious	19
134	Shouts, raises voice, or uses derogatory language	11
135	Shows marked interest in opposite sex	57
136	Witty and charming	23
137	Reports feeling cheerful	8
138	Assumes unusual postures	78
139	Has obvious hallucinations	27

TABLE 43

ARRAY FOR CURRENT BEHAVIOR STEREOTYPE FACTOR B
(Highest and Lowest 15 Items)

Rank	Item	Item Number
1	States that he (she) feels unreal	30
2	Isolated and withdrawn	109
3	Tries to "do good" for other patients and to help the staff with their work	122
4	Sweating decreased	64
5	Avoids using color in work—uses dark, somber colors	137
6	Speech slurred and mumbled	88
7	Has bad taste in mouth	96
8	Prefers to remain by him(her)self	110
9	Acts ingratiatingly with staff	121
10	Expresses appreciation for care and interest of staff	115
11	Has excessively dry skin	59
12	Stays in bed much of the time	76
13	Eats alone in room	56
14	Holds self stiff and rigid	83
15	Thought processes are slow and retarded	41
125	Restless (has difficulty in remaining still)	5
126	Pays attention to grooming	100
127	Feels more comfortable after hospitalization	119
128	Limited and repetitive thought content	42
129	Complains constantly about hospital, staff, food, etc.	113
130	Complains of boredom	2
131	Eats with group in lounge	51
132	Enters into activity with group on unit	108

(Continued)

TABLE 43 *(Continued)*

Rank	Item	Item Number
133	Eats breakfast	53
134	Makes realistic demands of personnel	136
135	Communicates with men	125
136	Memory is good	32
137	Communicates with women	126
138	Communicates with staff	102
139	Communicates with other patients	103

TABLE 44

ARRAY FOR CURRENT BEHAVIOR STEREOTYPE FACTOR C
(Highest and Lowest 15 Items)

Rank	Item	Item Number
1	Speech slurred and mumbled	88
2	Has obvious delusions	28
3	Has flat, masklike face	80
4	Picks at self or clothing	81
5	Never smiles	6
6	Sobs (no lacrimation)	4
7	Has obvious hallucinations	27
8	Composed	17
9	Sits alone very quietly	75
10	Misidentifies people	31
11	Assumes unusual postures	78
12	Complains of boredom	2
13	Eats lunch	54
14	Complains of being unable to cry	15
15	Feels more comfortable after hospitalization	119
125	Seems alert and responsive	123
126	Clean and neat	98
127	Sweating increased	63
128	Wrings hands	74
129	Communicates with men	125
130	Nauseated	46
131	Response to similar situation varies	128
132	Provokes anger in staff or patients	18
133	Shows evidence of humor (responds appropriately to humorous situations and/or can make other people laugh)	16

(Continued)

TABLE 44 *(Continued)*

Rank	Item	Item Number
134	Makes realistic demands of personnel	136
135	Makes excessive demands	104
136	Approaches other people as a source of help	130
137	Shows bloating and belching	50
138	Clinging	105
139	Dizzy spells	97

TABLE 45

ARRAY FOR CURRENT BEHAVIOR STEREOTYPE FACTOR D
(Highest and Lowest 15 Items)

Rank	Item	Item Number
1	Especially sensitive to noise	95
2	Unconvincing gaiety	25
3	Seen to smile at some time during observation	7
4	Becomes involved in detail	133
5	Makes excessive demands	104
6	Acts ingratiatingly with staff	121
7	Is easily distractable	85
8	Eats with group in lounge	51
9	Communicates with other patients	103
10	Complains of boredom	2
11	Changes tasks frequently	79
12	Has flat, masklike face	80
13	Tries to "do good" for other patients and to help staff with their work	122
14	Restless (has difficulty in remaining still)	5
15	Misidentifies people	31
125	Tremulous	86
126	Physical examination is essentially negative	139
127	Prefers to remain by him(her)self	110
128	Works primarily by himself	135
129	Communicates with staff	102
130	Appetite poor	43
131	Limited and repetitive thought content	42
132	Shows little or no interest in opposite sex	58
133	Cries (lacrimation)	3

(Continued)

TABLE 45 *(Continued)*

Rank	Item	Item Number
134	Never smiles	66
135	Little attention to detail	134
136	Isolated and withdrawn	109
137	Eats alone in room	56
138	Stays in bed much of the time	76
139	Clinging	105

CHAPTER 11

Personal Data Correlations

EACH PATIENT'S RECORD CONTAINS SOME PERSONAL
data such as age, amount of education, religious affiliation, and
others. Analyses were made to determine whether or not the personal data would show correlations with feelings and concerns and
current behavior factor scorers. The results are shown in Tables 46
and 47.

RESULTS OF THE ANALYSES

Table 46 presents the mean factor scores for patients receiving
three different treatments and for patients with different religious
affiliations. In order to determine whether differences are "real"
or merely due to chance, statistical tests were made, but they did
not reach acceptable levels of significance, so that the differences
are only suggestive.

As approximate yardsticks for interpreting Table 46, it would
be unsafe to interpret differences on the current behavior factors
which are less than .30 and differences less than .50 on the feelings
and concerns factors. By these standards, it is apparent that most
differences are very small. It may be that there is a real difference
on current behavior Factor 10 (clinging, requests for love) between the group who received electric shock therapy from psychoanalytically oriented therapists and the groups who received psy-

TABLE 46

AVERAGE FACTOR SCORES FOR VARIOUS GROUPS OF PATIENTS
ON CURRENT BEHAVIOR AND FEELINGS AND CONCERNS FACTORS

	Number in group	Current Behavior Factors										Feelings and Concerns Factors				
		1	2	3	4	5	6	7	8	9	10	1	2	3	4	5
Received EST* from Psa-oriented† Therapists	15	.54	.45	.87	.25	.17	.28	.57	.33	.21	.22	1.52	0.91	1.01	1.87	1.08
Treated by Psa-Oriented Therapists with no EST	25	.43	.25	.70	.17	.16	.23	.41	.35	.11	.51	1.53	1.02	1.20	2.00	1.10
Received neither treatment	56	.44	.38	.75	.21	.22	.33	.58	.23	.17	.41	1.45	0.92	1.05	1.96	1.19
Religion																
Jewish	60	.40	.34	.73	.22	.22	.30	.53	.27	.19	.40	1.41	1.00	1.03	1.90	1.10
Protestant	20	.62	.43	.86	.18	.19	.28	.53	.34	.15	.41	1.77	1.07	1.26	2.18	1.35
Catholic	16	.43	.31	.73	.21	.12	.30	.53	.25	.08	.41	1.42	0.59	1.06	1.89	1.07

*EST means electric shock therapy
†Psa means psychoanalytic

chotherapy from psychoanalytically oriented therapists but no electric shock therapy. Perhaps the pitiful pleas for love influenced the therapists to persist longer with psychotherapy and delay or forego electric shock treatment. No other difference between treatment groups is revealed by our technique.

Regarding religious affiliation, there is only one difference large enough to consider seriously. Catholics appear to be lower on feelings and concerns Factor 2 than are Protestants and Jews. However, some evidence is presented in Table 47 to suggest that the apparent difference may be due only to chance.

Table 47 presents correlations between personal data and scorers on the current behavior and feelings and concerns factors. The lower portion of the table presents correlations among the personal data categories. The first six columns in the table show information that was provided in another form in Table 46. Here, methods of treatment and religious affiliation have each been analyzed as three dichotomous categories. That is, with religious affiliation, Catholics are compared with Protestants and Jews combined, Protestants are compared with Catholics and Jews combined, and Jews are compared with Catholics and Protestants combined. Treatment methods were handled similarly. The advantage of this method of analysis is that the results can be shown as correlation coefficients. It is easy to grasp the meaning of correlation coefficients and relatively easy to test for statistical significance. The disadvantage of using this method of analysis is that it compares one group with two other groups lumped together, which sometimes makes the interpretation of results difficult. However, armed with the information in Table 50, correct interpretations of Table 47 are facilitated.

Age, amount of education, and time before report are all continuous variables, and, consequently, correlation is the natural procedure to apply. Sex is, of course, dichotomous. A positive correlation means that men are higher as a group in the particular factor, and a negative correlation means that women are higher. Whereas, for the first six columns in the table, the level required for statistical significance varies somewhat from column to column, in general it is unsafe to interpret correlations less than .30. In the last four columns the level required for statistical significance is uniform: correlations less than .25 should not be interpreted.

Regarding treatment methods and religious affiliation, the results in Table 47 confirm the interpretations made of Table 2 since the correlations are generally very small. There is one striking and probably important finding in Table 46: age correlates positively with the first nine current behavior factors, and three of the correlations are well above the required level of statistical significance. Age correlates −.10 with Factor 10, which is oriented toward "good" or "pleasant" behavior. When the factor analysis was done, we could easily have turned the factor around to the "negative" and then the correlation would be +.10. The direct importance of this finding is that it shows that there is a tendency for older patients to show more of the aggravated outward signs of depression than younger patients. The finding also has a broader import which will be discussed later.

Education tends to correlate with the "good" current behavior indicator, the only exception being the correlation of .09 with Factor 8. However, the correlations here are not so large as those found for age. There is one marked correlation for sex, the correlation of .37 with Factor 8. In other words, male patients as a group are higher on the factor indicating psychomotor rigidity.

One caution that must be exercised in studying correlations like those in Table 47 is that the variables are usually confounded with one another to some extent. Thus, it may be found that women have more education than men or that older people are more often Protestant than Catholic or Jewish, and so on. In order to offset the confounding, "partial" correlations were obtained, which are presented in the bottom of Table 47. These show, for example, the correlations between education and the 15 factors, when age is held constant. Most of the correlations there are very low.

TABLE 47

CORRELATIONS BETWEEN FACTOR SCORES AND PERSONAL DATA INFORMATION

	EST from Psa-oriented Therapists	Treated by Psa-oriented Therapists with no EST	Got neither treatment	Catholic	Protestant	Jewish	Age	Sex	Education	Time spent in hospital before rating was made
Feelings and Concerns Factors										
I	.02	.04	-.05	-.04	.21	-.14	-.07	-.02	.00	.18
II	-.02	.07	-.04	-.24	.10	.10	.04	.16	.02	-.08
III	-.04	.10	-.05	-.01	.13	-.10	-.01	-.17	.04	.13
IV	-.05	.03	.00	-.04	.14	-.09	-.05	-.12	.03	.06
V	-.06	-.05	.09	-.07	.19	-.11	.05	-.04	-.14	-.09
Current Behavior Factors										
1	.12	-.04	-.15	-.02	.27	-.21	.20	-.15	-.16	.16
2	.13	-.19	.08	-.06	.11	-.05	.29	.15	-.16	.01
3	.19	-.12	-.04	-.05	.21	-.14	.33	.07	-.16	.05
4	.08	-.09	.02	.00	-.06	.05	.11	-.01	-.10	.18
5	-.04	-.09	.11	-.14	-.02	.13	.30	-.16	-.13	.01
6	-.03	-.12	.13	.01	-.04	.03	.21	-.05	-.16	.02
7	.05	-.22	.16	.00	.00	.00	.13	-.16	-.16	.03
8	.09	.18	-.23	-.05	.13	-.07	.10	.37	.09	-.07
9	.09	-.13	.05	-.17	-.03	.16	.19	-.02	-.19	-.15
10	-.23	.17	.02	.00	.00	.01	-.10	-.11	.15	-.13

(Continued)

TABLE 47 (Continued)

Personal Data Information	EST from Psa-oriented Therapists	Treated by Psa-oriented Therapists with no EST	Got neither treatment	Catholic	Protestant	Jewish	Age	Sex	Education	Time spent in hospital before rating was made
Got EST from Psa-oriented Therapists				-.12	.20	-.08	.14	.05	-.09	.09
Treated by Psa-oriented Therapists with no EST				-.07	-.01	.07	-.08	.05	.12	.00
Got neither Treatment				.15	-.14	.00	-.03	-.08	-.04	-.07
Catholic	-.12	-.07	.15				-.40	-.09	-.01	.05
Protestant	.20	-.01	-.14				.15	.02	.00	.13
Jewish	-.08	.07	.00				.17	.05	.01	-.15
Age	.14	-.08	-.03	-.40	.15	.17		.16	-.35	.08
Sex	.05	.05	-.08	-.09	.02	.05	.16		.07	.00
Education	-.09	.12	-.04	-.01	.00	.01	-.35	.07		-.10
Time spent in hospital before rating was made	.09	.00	-.07	.05	.13	-.15	.08	.00	-.10	

There is a substantial negative correlation (—.40) between being Catholic and age. In other words, the Catholic patients were, as a group, younger than the Protestants and Jews. There may be some simpler explanation for the difference, or it may be that Catholics tend to have depressions earlier in life than do Jews and Protestants. The data at hand is not nearly substantial enough to support the latter explanation. However, it is important to keep such possibilities in mind for subsequent studies.

There is a correlation of —.35 between age and education, which indicates that, as a group, the older patients have less education than younger patients. A correlation of about that size is usually found in the general population for adults above 25 years of age. The correlation between age and education in this study probably accounts for the tendency for education to correlate negatively with the "bad" current behavior indicators. In other words, if all of the patients were of about the same age, it is doubtful that amount of education would correlate with the current behavior factors.

There is an over-all trend in Table 47 that tends to support previous suggestions about relationships between the feelings and concerns factors and the current behavior factors. Previously it was suggested that the extent and form of the depression, as evidenced in the former, is only incidental to the external manifestations of the depression, as evidenced in the latter. Further, it was suggested that the external manifestation is determined by circumstances in the life of the patient which have little, if anything, to do with the basic pathology. If this is so, one would expect to find larger correlations between the current behavior factors and personal data than between the feelings and concerns factors and personal data. The results in Table 47 tend to support the hypothesis. The trend can be seen by comparing the first five rows in Table 47 with the next ten rows. Although in both sections of the table correlations are generally low, they are, on the average, lower in the feelings and concerns section. None of the correlations between these factors and personal data are statistically significant, and few are even close. In the current behavior section of the table, four correlations are statistically significant, and many are close to the required level. Also the trend shown by the age variable in this section is too definite to be ignored.

CONCLUSIONS

Although no final decision should be reached on the basis of this data, the indication is that personal data items tend to correlate with current behavior factors more than with feelings and concerns factors. Of course, at the present time the hypothesis is too crude to be tested. First it would be necessary to specify the kinds of personal data that would be expected to correlate with the two sets of factors.

Two methodological points should be made about these results. First, some of the personal data was not recorded precisely enough. For example, from the records it was difficult to determine the amount of education of some patients. The best procedure would have been to record the number of years of completed schooling. In many cases education was recorded as "some college" or as "failed to complete high school." This made it necessary in some instances to conjecture about the exact years of education. Similar conjectures had to be made about some of the other personal data information. Such uncertainties inevitably tend to obscure differences between groups and to lower correlations. However, it is doubtful that the imprecision in this study was large enough to hide definite relationships.

A second methodological point to be made is that a relatively narrow range of personal data was noted. Although personal data such as sex, age, and education are the obvious ones to study, it may be that a broader range of personal data information would produce some interesting relations with the factors.

SUMMARY

Correlations between a limited amount of personal data with the 15 factors developed from our two trait lists were generally not statistically significant. Only suggestive conclusions may be derived, such as that the clinging depressive receives shock treatment less often or not as early; older patients have more serious and aggravated behavioral signs of depression; current behavior factors are more highly correlated with personal data than feelings and concerns. A much more detailed and careful study of the significance of demographic factors in correlation with depression factors needs to be done.

~~~~~~~~~~~~~~~~~~~~~~~~~~~~~~~~~~~~

CHAPTER 12

Factor Patterns

THE NEXT ANALYSIS WAS TO DETERMINE WHAT correlations exist among and between the two sets of factors. The results are reported in Table 48. The box of correlations in the upper left of the table shows all possible relations among the five feelings and concerns factors; the box in the lower right contains all possible correlations among the ten current behavior factors. The boxes in the lower left and in the upper right both show the correlations between the two sets of factors.

With 96 patients, a correlation of .25 can be considered statistically significant. However, in the present case, we do not take correlations seriously unless they are about .40 or higher. The reason for applying a higher standard here is that some correlation between factors is to be expected, because they all concern various forms of pathology. Only if there is a substantial correlation between two factors does it provide important information.

CORRELATIONS AMONG FEELINGS AND CONCERNS FACTORS

In the feelings and concerns group, the major finding is the correlations of .67 between Factors I and III. Patients who are high in Factor I tend, as a group, to be high on Factor III, and vice versa for patients who are low in Factor I. In other words, dismal hopelessness and guilt feelings usually appear together; however,

TABLE 48

CORRELATIONS BETWEEN FEELINGS AND CONCERNS AND CURRENT BEHAVIOR FACTORS

	Feelings and Concerns Factors					Current Behavior Factors									
	I	II	III	IV	V	1	2	3	4	5	6	7	8	9	10
Feelings and Concerns															
1		.24	.67	.36	.36	.08	.17	.16	-.05	.07	.05	.16	-.05	-.10	-.06
2	.24		.31	.06	.19	-.11	.06	-.03	-.15	.06	-.12	.23	-.06	.06	.12
3	.67	.31		.35	.26	-.04	.01	.05	-.08	.10	.03	.24	-.21	-.10	.06
4	.36	.06	.35		-.05	-.02	.10	.02	.10	.06	.05	.19	-.26	.05	-.01
5	.36	.19	.26	-.05		-.08	-.02	.11	-.08	.25	.09	.15	-.04	.07	.02
Current Behavior															
1	.08	-.11	-.04	-.02	-.08		.47	.46	.15	.22	.27	.04	.24	.09	-.40
2	.17	.06	.01	.10	-.02	.47		.52	.19	.20	.49	.05	.36	.26	-.36
3	.16	-.03	.05	.02	.11	.46	.52		-.01	.07	.23	.07	.21	.04	-.30
4	-.05	-.15	-.08	.10	-.08	.15	.19	-.01		.28	.24	.01	-.02	.28	-.62
5	.07	.06	.10	.06	.25	.22	.20	.07	.28		.32	.39	-.20	.39	-.02
6	.05	-.12	.03	.05	.09	.27	.49	.23	.24	.32		.21	.02	.43	-.21
7	.16	.23	.24	.19	.15	.04	.05	.07	.01	.39	.21		-.29	.15	.15
8	-.05	-.06	-.21	-.26	-.04	.24	.36	.21	-.02	-.20	.02	-.29		-.02	-.23
9	-.10	.06	-.10	.05	.07	.09	.26	.04	.28	.39	.43	.15	-.02		-.08
10	-.06	.12	.06	-.01	.02	-.40	-.36	-.30	-.62	-.02	-.21	.15	-.23	-.08	

the relationship is far from perfect, and it will not be at all surprising to find, for example, a patient who is very high in Factor III and less than average on Factor I. Factor I tends to correlate at least moderately with the other four feelings and concerns factors, which supports the hypothesis stated previously that Factor I is the central or basic theme of depression as manifested in feelings and concerns traits.

CORRELATIONS AMONG CURRENT BEHAVIOR FACTORS

In the current behavior group there are numerous correlations of .40 or higher. Factors 1, 2, and 3 form a little cluster, in which all correlations are positive and substantial. These all have to do with withdrawal, isolation, slowing of speech and thought. Factor 10 is correlated negatively with all of the others except 7, and some of the negative correlations are fairly large. In other words persons who are high in Factor 10 tend to be low in all of the other factors (except 7). Thus agitation and clinging are associated. On the other hand, there is a strong negative correlation ($-.62$) between Factors 4 and 10, which is to be expected since provocative angry behavior does not usually go with clinging pleas for love.

CORRELATIONS BETWEEN BOTH SETS OF FACTORS

Looking at the correlations between the feelings and concerns and the current behavior factors, the conclusion is that, for all practical purposes, the two sets of factors are independent. Correlations which are found could easily have been obtained by chance alone. That is, if instead of having psychiatrists rate the patients, dice were tossed to obtain the feelings and concerns ratings and coins were flipped to obtain the current behavior ratings, we would expect to find correlations of the kind shown in Table 48. Even if in a larger study it is found that some of the correlations between the two sets of factors are statistically significant, the results in Table

48 indicate strongly that the correlations are, in general, of no practical consequence. Since reliability in the ratings of each set of factors was high, low reliability cannot account for the lack of correlations.

DISCUSSION OF THE RESULTS

The independence of the two sets of factors has some interesting implications. First, it is obvious that the distinction which was made between feelings and concerns and current behavior traits in the early stages of the research was very useful. If the distinction had not been made, and the two kinds of traits had been mingled in the early Q-technique studies, the results would have been unproductive.

With regard to the psychology of depression, the analysis shows that depression as manifested in the feelings and concerns traits is almost completely unrelated to depression as manifested in the current behavior traits. This has far-reaching implications—if we knew what it meant. One possibility is that, among depressive patients, overt behavior patterns are not indicants of "inner experiences," as for example internal anxiety (IV) and external agitation (7). However, it must be remembered that depressive patients probably have considerably more of the current behavior factors than do normals. The point is that these factors are not differentially indicative of what is "going on inside" depressed patients. There is then the further suggestion that physical symptoms and modes of social response are, in a sense, unimportant in the differentiation of depressions. One way of looking at it is that the depressed patient has a number of modes available for manifesting or expressing the pathology in physiological states and in social interaction; and the mode, or modes, which the patient "chooses" are determined by considerations other than the nature and extent of the depression itself. This was also suggested in the last chapter by the fact that behaviors were correlated with personal data while feelings were not.

Another possible explanation for the failure of correlations between factor groups to appear is that patients tend to fall into "clusters" or "types" in such a way as to obscure over-all relationships. For example, men and women might represent such "types." Considering the men separately, it might be found, for example, that there is a strong positive correlation between age and feelings and concerns Factor I. Considering the women separately, it might be found that there is a *negative* correlation between Factor I and age. Then, in any over-all comparison, combining the data for men and women, the correlation between age and Factor I would be near zero. Because of such possibilities it was decided to perform an analysis of factor patterns to determine if, in fact, there is a tendency for "typing" or "clustering" in depressed patients.

DERIVATION OF FACTOR PATTERNS

In order to study these questions it was necessary to perform an elaborate and unusual form of mathematical analysis which is described briefly below. Essentially what we did was to factor-analyze factors. Each of 96 patients had scores on each of 15 factors. We then factor-analyzed patients, as contrasted to our previous analyses in which we factor-analyzed traits.* In this way we hoped to determine which patients "go together," in the same sense as in previous studies we determined which traits go together.

Because of the type of analysis performed, it is not as easy to

---

* The novel feature of the analysis was that it was a "raw score" factor analysis, a point which only the statistical specialist would find either meaningful or intriguing. If instead of using raw scores we had used correlations or covariances we would have thrown away pertinent information. The difficulty in using raw score factor analysis is that such analyses have not been fully programed for electronic computers, and some of the routine methods of analysis do not apply.

A 96x96 matrix of raw score crossproducts was factor-analyzed by the controid method, and ten factors were obtained. These were then subjected to various analytic methods of rotation on the digital computer. None of the analytic results gave satisfactory solutions. Consequently, it was necessary to perform the rotations by hand, resulting in four usable factors each of which is a pattern of the 15 factors found earlier.

interpret the factor loadings as it is to interpret the loadings given
when correlations are analyzed as was done in all previous analyses.
The loadings can range anywhere from .00 up to about 4.00. A
person can have high loadings on all of the factor patterns or he
can have low loadings on all of them. The size of the loading indicates the extent to which the particular patient has a set of loadings
on the 15 factors in current behavior and feelings and concerns
which is similar to the pattern of loadings typifying the particular
factor pattern.

The most meaningful way to interpret the loadings is in a relative sense. That is, if a patient has a higher loading on Factor
Pattern A than the majority of the patients, it means that he is
relatively high in that factor pattern. If a patient has a higher
loading on Factor Pattern B than on any of the other three factor
patterns, it means that he is more like Pattern B than he is like
any of the other factor patterns. It is considerably more difficult
to interpret the results of complex analyses of this kind than it
is to interpret more conventional factor-analytic results. Although
the mathematical procedures are straightforward, and, in this
case, the ideal ones to apply, the results are complicated to the
point of straining the cognitive capacity of the investigators.

As would be expected, the results show that most patients are
"mixtures" of the four patterns in varying degrees. In order to
interpret the results, it is necesary to have some persons who are
relatively "pure" for each factor pattern. For Factor Pattern A,
there is a considerable number of relatively "pure" types. For
Pattern B, there are some patients who predominate in that pattern, but most of them have sizable loadings on Factor Pattern A
also. For Patterns C and D, it was not possible to find "pure"
patients.

Ideally, in order to interpret the results and in order to use
the factor patterns henceforth, each patient should have a high
loading on one, and only one, of the factor patterns. However, this
never happens, and the most we can expect is to find a statistical

tendency for patients to be "strong" in certain patterns and relatively "weak" in other patterns.

Because of the complexity of the analysis and of the results, it is rather difficult to give precise meanings to the factor loadings for particular patients. However, it is meaningful to examine what is held in common by the patients who are "most pure" on each of the factor patterns. These results are shown, in Table 49, as the end result of all the analyses that were undertaken. It shows the average scores for the "pure patients" on each of the 15 factors. For comparison purposes, the average scores for *all* patients are also shown.

Table 49 shows for example that the patients who are relatively "pure" for Factor Pattern A have an average score of .58 on feelings and concerns Factor I. The patients relatively "pure" for Factor Pattern D have an average score on feelings and concerns Factor I of .66, which is slightly higher than that for the "pure patients" on Factor Pattern A. Table 49 also shows that the average score for all 96 patients on feelings and concerns Factor I is .49.

There are three possible ways of interpreting the results. First, interpretations can be made of the *absolute* size of average factor scores. For example, in Table 49 Factor Pattern B has an average score on feelings and concerns Factor IV of .94, which is nearly as high as it could be. Factor Pattern A has an average score of only .02 on current behavior Factor 10, which is close to zero. In this way interpretations can be made of the absolute size of average factor scores shown in Table 49.

Interpretations can also be made of the *relative* size of average factor scores shown in Table 49, and there are two ways to make such comparisons. First, factor patterns can be compared with one another. For example, it can be seen that on feelings and concerns Factor IV, Factor Pattern D has a much higher average score than does Factor Pattern C (.92 as opposed to .58). Second, comparisons can be made between particular factor patterns and the average scores for all 96 patients, shown in the last column of

Table 49. For example, it is seen that for current behavior Factor 1, Factor Pattern A is above average, B is below average, C is near average, and D is way below average.

In order to interpret the results given in Table 49 it is necessary to restudy the previous results: (1) description of the feelings and concerns factors, and (2) the description of the current behavior factors, since scores on those factors were used in the factor pattern analysis. Originally, factor scores on the current behavior factors were stated in percentages; i.e., a score of .00 meant the lowest possible score and a score of 1.00 meant the highest possible score. The feelings and concerns factors were scaled differently. They ranged from .00 to 3.00. For this analysis, and for the results reported in Table 49, the feelings and concerns factor scores are also scaled on a percentage continuum, with .00 meaning "lowest possible" and 1.00 meaning "highest possible."

FACTOR PATTERN PROFILES

The next logical step is to use the factors from the two trait lists of feelings and concerns and current behavior from which the factor patterns were derived in order to develop profiles of patients within each pattern. It is of course understood that each patient may have characteristics of more than one pattern, as they do of more than one factor. Actually, they usually have a heavy loading in only one. Some patients may be considered as relatively "pure" for one factor pattern only. There are 13 such patients in Pattern A, 11 in Pattern B, 7 in Pattern C, and only 4 in Pattern D. This gives a rough idea of frequency distribution in patterns of 38 patients who are relatively "pure" on one pattern, leaving 58 who show no particular pattern affinity.

We shall now outline the patterns using the applications applied to the five feelings and concerns factors and the ten current behavior factors. To these profiles we append the clinical characteristics that we *think* would be characteristic although each of these statements is only an hypothesis to be tested by correlations achieved in future research.

Factor Pattern A

On feelings and concerns these persons are above the average of all patients in Factors I, III, and IV. They are dismal and hopeless, with loss of self-esteem, and to some degree feel guilty. Their behavior is withdrawn, isolated, and apathetic; speech and thinking are slowed; there are evidences of cognitive disturbances. However, they are *not* hypochondriacal, anxious, clinging, and love-seeking, nor do they have many somatic symptoms.

These traits describe a person who is moderately sick and close to the common stereotype of depression. The absence of large amounts of gloomy affect and the apathy, uncomplaining attitude without efforts at projection, attempts at restitution, or clinging demands for love give the appearance of an "empty" person who has "given up." Yet the moderate degree of hopelessness in spite of the withdrawal and apathy does not suggest the so-called psychotic depression.

Such a profile recalls from empirical experience a premorbid compulsive personality precipitated into a depression by internal changes or by aging and the attendant external alterations of sexual, familial, and economic roles, hence occurring in middle life. These patients respond poorly to psychotherapy and usually receive electric shock therapy or other somatotherapy. They have a tendency to relapse and usually have several hospital admissions during their lifetimes.

Factor Pattern B

Patients in this pattern have high loadings on feelings and concerns factors indicating dismal, hopeless attitudes and low self-esteem, considerable guilt feelings and almost as much anxiety as possible, but little more than average use of an external event as a focus of blame and for feelings of being rejected. In current behavior two factors dominate; agitation and clinging demands for attention. There are lower than average loadings on all other behavioral characteristics such as slowed speech, impaired thinking, hypochondriasis, and psychosomatic symptoms.

This pattern suggests a fairly well-integrated premorbid personality whose equilibrium has been broken by some external event which cued off a mobilization of repressed aggression. The resulting guilt feelings and self-punishment mobilize attempts at restitution to make up for wrongs done, rationalized by recall of many past incidents. At the same time there is considerable pleading for help and affection. The projective mechanism of blaming others is only slightly used.

Patients within this pattern are helped by support and kindness although they temporarily feel better after externally furnished punishment. In the height of their agitation they are sleepless, anorexic, and suicidal. Their clinging demands lead their families to institute early hospitalization. Such patients complain bitterly, demand drugs insatiably, and are benefited by tranquilizers. Some can endure the anxiety signalling eruption of repressed hostile feelings and do well in psychotherapy.

Factor Pattern C

These patients do not exceed the average scores on the feelings and concerns trait list except for Factor V indicating a feeling of not being loved. Thus they have less than average depressed affect, guilt, or anxiety. In current behavior they are outstanding in their agitated, demanding, hypochondriac complaints, associated also with psychosomatic symptoms. Cognitive functions seem disturbed.

The striking aspect of this pattern is the low loading on dismal and hopeless affect in contrast to the active irrational complaining attitudes. This is the picture of the hypochondriac, where attention is diverted to his own body although seemingly rationalized by some observable somatic manifestations.

Herein lies the difficult differential diagnosis from complainers who are somehow aware of an inner destructive process in spite of negative medical examinations. Many of these "know" of their illness before it is discovered, too late. In general patients with the hypochondriacal syndrome have been seriously disturbed all their lives, often with a variety of "borderline" symptoms or with some schizoid features. They are precipitated into depression by actual external losses or by approaching aging. They seem to benefit, but only temporarily, by support, reassurance, and drugs. Electric shock treatment often worsens the condition. In rare cases prolonged psychotherapy is helpful.

Factor Pattern D

This pattern is characterized by high loadings on feelings and concerns traits of gloom, hopelessness, and anxiety with some guilt feelings; but these patients do not cling or demand attention. They thus resemble the B factor pattern. But they are distinguished by current behavior characteristics most of which are low, except for Factor 4 describing demanding provocative behavior. These patients are not withdrawn, continually seeking affection, hypochondriacal, nor do they have somatic symptoms. They are the "angry depressives" whose behavior does not suggest an etiologic component of "repressed aggression."

The premorbid personalities of these patients are typically narcissistic and overaggressive. They "rule the roost" at home, in business, or in their social settings. Precipitated by frustration or inability to continue this pattern for external reasons they become depressed and attempt to influence the environment through their illness. Suicidal thoughts are frequent and serious. They are difficult management problems for hospital personnel and treatment is fraught with dangers and disappointments. The former constitutes the eruption of rage expressed by suicide. The disappointment is inherent in the never-ending compulsion to be on top or to be the best, which intereferes with psychotherapy.

FURTHER USES OF FACTOR PATTERNS

Interpretations of factor patterns should have an impact on psychiatric theory and practice and can be used in additional research. People can be scored on the patterns, and such pattern scores can be correlated with indices such as demographic characteristics, background data, and the effects of various forms of treatment. The patterns might also eventually have practical usefulness as psychometric devices to be used in the diagnosis and treatment of patients.

Because it is found that there are some "patterning" or "typing" tendencies in the data, it should not be assumed that the individual factors are no longer useful. In all future studies, before trying to relate variables to pattern scores, it would be wiser first to try to relate variables to the individual factor measurements.

SUMMARY

Correlations among factors from the feelings and concerns check list revealed that dismal affect and hopelessness are associated with guilt feelings and correlated moderately with the other four factors, indicating Factor I as the central or basic theme in depressions.

In the current behavior, Factors 1, 2, and 3 form a cluster indicating that withdrawal, isolation, and slowing of speech and thought are associated. Likewise, agitation and clinging, Factors 10 and 7, go together as contrasted with a negative relation between 4 (demanding, angry behavior) and 10 (clinging pleas for love).

Correlations between the two sets of factors from our two check lists show that they are independent from each other. Behavior seems not to be correlated with inner feelings more than with personal predetermined types of expression.

By means of a complicated mathematical procedure, factor patterns were derived from the sum of factors from each list, 15 in all. The result was the discovery of four factor patterns in which individual patients can be found who are relatively "pure." These patterns can be the basis of clinical profiles from which hypotheses may be drawn regarding premorbid personality, precipitating factors, psychodynamics, course, responses to various forms of treatment, relapses, demographic data, etc.

TABLE 49

AVERAGE SCORES ON 10 CURRENT BEHAVIOR
AND 5 FEELINGS AND CONCERNS FACTORS
FOR EACH OF 4 FACTOR PATTERNS AND FOR ALL PATIENTS

Factor	Average Score				
	Factor Pattern				All
	A	B	C	D	Patients
Current behavior					
1 Isolated and withdrawn	.76*	.25	.54	.07	.45
2 Speech and thought slowed	.67*	.13	.38	.13	.36
3 Apathetic	.95*	.65	.71	.35	.76
4 Demanding and provocative	.32	.03	.51*	.61*	.21
5 Hypochondriac	.16	.18	.69*	.04	.20
6 Cognitive disturbances	.56*	.15	.59*	.09	.30
7 Agitation	.39	.70*	.90*	.46	.53
8 Thought confusion	.40	.13	.49*	.10	.16
9 Psychosomatic symptoms	.14	.13	.49*	.10	.16
10 Clinging, demanding	.02	.86*	.36	.00	.41
Feelings and Concerns					
I Dismal, hopeless, "bad"	.58*	.66*	.38	.66*	.49
II Projection to external events	.24	.42	.35	.42	.32
III Guilty feelings	.43*	.62*	.26	.49*	.36
IV Anxiety	.69*	.94*	.58	.92*	.65
V Clinging appeals for love	.36	.36	.48*	.32	.38

*Loadings of factors characteristic of pattern

224

General Summary

PSYCHIATRISTS IN THE EARLY SCIENTIFIC-MEDICAL era of the nineteenth century were concerned with description and classification. The psychoanalytic discoveries of the twentieth century have led them to concentrate more on formulations of individual psychodynamics. As a result, progress toward more accurate clinical definition of the depressive syndrome, which would also lead to isolation of subcategories of this vast global construct, has been slow. With empirically sound subdivisions of depression, meaningful correlations with nonpsychological data would probably further our knowledge of etiology, course, prognosis, and therapy (Introduction and Chapter 1).

SUMMARY OF THE RESEARCH

For our empirical study we set up two major questions, the answers to which could improve the clinical definition of depressions and establish significant subgroups. Furthermore, we attempted to determine why patients became depressed. If answerable, these questions could also help isolate the elements concerned with etiological diagnosis. We first formulated the necessary questions which might enable us to obtain essential data from patients' reports and from direct observations of their behavior (Chapter 2).

We should like to re-emphasize the fact that we did not define

225

depression in advance of our investigations. We assumed that the diagnosis of depression as a syndrome made by two psychiatrists on admission and at discharge represented the way in which contemporary psychiatrists isolated this entity from the large number of mental conditions. Nowhere in our trait lists, symptoms, or factors is the term *depression* to be found, since depression was the syndrome under investigation and not one of the component feelings or behaviors. Instead, sadness, hopelesness, anxiety, etc., are constituents of the feelings and concerns trait list, making it possible to define what psychiatrists call depression (a syndrome) and avoiding the circular process of reasoning such as: "he has a depression because he is depressed." We attempted to define what psychiatrists call depressions by isolating their component affective and behavioral traits and studying their combinations. Thus in a sense we started out with the basic assumption that clinical descriptions from antiquity to now, by their monotonously repetitive content, have confirmed and reconfirmed the fact that such a syndrome really exists.

After interrogating and observing, in a pilot study, 21 depressed patients behind a one-way screen, the resulting case reports were translated into forms suitable for statistical study. This consisted of a 111-trait list of feelings and concerns and an 87-trait list of current behaviors which were prepared for Q-sorting. We also used four check lists of symptoms, dream types, precipitating events, and meanings of precipitating events (Chapter 3).

The feelings and concerns check list was highly reliable and permitted us to use the rank order of agreements for a profile of the combined feelings of depressive patients. We could also with assurance factor-analyze the data which uncovered three factors. Each factor contained highly loaded traits that permitted us to draw a sharply defined clinical picture of each subgroup and to exemplify them with case reports from our series of 21 patients. On the other hand, the reliability of ratings on the current behavior check list was too low to justify factor analysis. The reasons for failure to attain reliability were studied, and essentially they consisted in the greater interest of psychiatrists in inferences and interpretations and their neglect of observations, descriptions, and adequate reporting of what they saw (Chapter 4).

Analyses of check lists concerned with dreams and premorbid personality were unsuccessful because of the paucity of dreams experienced, remembered, or reported and because information concerning premorbid personality from informants was too unreliable. Although psychiatrists, especialy those with psychoanalytic orientation, glibly pinpoint exact precipitating factors and formulate psychodynamics with great assurance, neither could be stated with confidence by the research group. In a scientific spirit of inquiry the investigators could not be sure or reach a consensus regarding the dynamic processes expressed by the symptoms of depression.

Q-sorts of stereotypes of feelings and concerns revealed one strong factor related only to Factor A of the pilot study. This describes the withdrawn, deeply depressed person and probably represents the core process of the syndrome. It was suggestive that this stereotypic patient was considered to be female. Obviously, the finding of Factors B and C among patients showed that psychiatrists could see beyond they stereotypes when considering particular patients. When data fell short for rating purposes, the mixture of stereotypes facilitated a heterogeneous filling of the gaps, further increasing the probability of variance in current behavior ratings. Thus not only do psychiatrists not rate behavior well, but they do not hold firm concepts of its patterns, at least in relation to depressions (Chapter 5).

When we turned to the full-scale study, with larger numbers of patients, the design of the research required alteration. Based on our experiences with the pilot study, the feelings and concerns and current behavior trait lists were radically modified. In the latter were included symptoms and precipitating events. Resident psychiatrists assigned to the patients on the nursing units filled out the feelings and concerns check list, and in addition one out of every four cases was also checked by a member of the research team. The current behavior check list was completed by the resident and the head nurse after at least five days' observation on the nursing unit. Again, each person involved in the research filled out a check list for his stereotype of a "typical" depression. We also included two other groups of patients as controls (Chapter 6).

In our larger series of depressed patients we have established the existence of five factors, which are patterns of traits descriptive of the feelings and concerns of these patients. These factors describe aspects of patients, and, although they indicate what may be predominant for some, any single patient may show evidence of more than one factor. They are not mutually exclusive; nor do they attempt to describe all aspects of any single patient. These factors may be characterized roughly as follows (Chapter 7):

I.   A factor describing characteristics of hopelessness, helplessness, failure, sadness, unworthiness, guilt, and internal suffering. There is no appeal to the outside world; no conviction that receiving anything from the environment would change how the patients feel. There is self-concept of "badness."

II. A factor describing characteristics of concern over material loss and an inner conviction that this feeling state (and the illness) could be changed if only the outside world would provide something.

III. A factor describing characteristics of guilt over wrongdoing by the patient, wishes to make restitution, and a feeling that the illness was brought on by the patient himself and is deserved.

IV. A factor describing characteristics of "free anxiety."

V.   A factor describing characteristics of envy, loneliness, martyred affliction, secondary gain, and gratification from the illness, and attempts, by provoking guilt, to force the world into making redress.

Admitted-depressed-and-discharged-depressed patients were high in Factors I and IV. Patients admitted with other diagnoses but discharged as depressed were high in Factor I and low in IV. Those who were admitted as depressives but discharged with another diagnosis were low in Factor I and high in IV, and those who on admission and discharge were not depressed showed only greater than average dependency on Factor V (Chapter 7).

The clinical interpretation of these factors suggests the hypotheses that Factor I is the essence of depression and hence its strength indicates the depth of the affective disturbance. The anxiety factor, IV, seems to be an indicator of activity in the process and perhaps also a signal of increasing or decreasing affective arousal. On the other hand, the remaining factors indicate varying attempts at defense and resolution of the depression. Hence Factor II indicates the projective defense, III the restitution resolution, and V the attempt by enslavery of external objects to deny anger, and secondarily to regain love. The control groups seems to show that the diagnosis of the depressive syndrome is contingent not only on the depressed affect but also on the presence of anxiety. In fact, in the presence of minimum sadness, anxiety is enough to weigh heavily for the diagnosis of depression. Finally, the nondepressed patient about whom there is no mistake in the admission diagnosis has in common with depressives the factor of dependency and demand for secondary gain (Chapter 7).

Studies also showed that the resident psychiatrists had a much higher degree of reliability on ratings of feelings and concerns than did the research psychiatrists.

Although we have mentioned several possible explanations for the discrepancies in reliability between residents and psychiatrists, we believe that the major reason is relatively simple. When we had any questions concerning the details of the pilot study, reference could be made to the protocols that described each patient thoroughly. The reliability differences described above suggested that we spot-check several patients' records in order to reconcile the conclusions drawn from observations achieved in direct interviews with the patients by both groups.

We were shocked at the paucity of information in the hospital charts. Not only were essential demographic data often missing, but only rarely did a patient come alive and be felt by the reader as a living human in trouble. We had known for some time that residents' recordings (as well as attending psychiatrists') were poor, but we had not been willing to see *how* deficient they were. Investigation into the records of other similar institutions revealed little difference. We have always shied away from histories written according to predetermined outlines, hoping to give free rein to spontaneity and individual expression and ordering. Subsequent to our discovery, repeated meetings with residents, urging, exhortation, and threats improved matters very little.

Although this point is not essential to the main thesis of this book and we do not wish to belabor the subject, it is of interest to conjecture why psychiatric hospitals with psychodynamic orientation should be so afflicted. It seems that the formulation by the resident has become all-important, and for this he has the facts or data derived from the patient well in mind but not graphically recorded. Neither he nor the attending psychiatrist conceive of the use of records for future research, but only for the barest essential notations. He speculates, manipulates, and formulates the data into an inference that gives him a sense of closure and satisfaction. Thus for the ratings of depressed patients the residents had the necessary information for high reliability; the research psychiatrists were much less reliable, and the hospital records were too vague or bare for the reconciliation of differences.

The stereotype of typical feelings and concerns in depression held in mind by the older men is more fixed compared to that of the residents, thereby perhaps giving the latter more "openness of mind." Even so, the only significant factor elicited from the ratings of stereotypes is I, which is the "common garden variety" of sad, hopeless, withdrawn, self-castigating, miserable, self-depreciating person (Chapter 8).

In our series of depressed patients we have established the existence of ten factors derived from the current behavior check list. These factors tend to be less sharp and distinct than the feelings and concerns factors, which reflects our finding that behavior is an area of less concern to psychiatrists and that our behavioral observations are not as accurate as our hearing, inferring, and interpretating content. Like the other factors, they are not mutually exclusive and any single patient participates in a number of factors. These behavioral factors may be characterized roughly as follows:

1. Characteristics of isolation, withdrawal, and apathy.
2. Characteristics of retardation, slowing of thought processes and speech, with little regard for personal appearance.
3. Characteristics of general retardation in behavior and gait, but less isolated and withdrawn than factor 1.
4. Characteristics of angry, provocative, complaining behavior.
5. Presence of somatic complaints, including dizzy spells and constipation.
6. Characteristics which sound like an "organic" syndrome: impairment of memory, confusion, inability to concentrate, and limited and repetitive thought content.
7. Characteristics of agitation, tremulousness, and restlessness.
8. Characteristics of rigidity and psychomotor retardation.
9. Presence of somatic symptoms such as dry skin and hair, along with minor abnormalities on physical examination.
10. Characteristics of ingratiating behavior: attempting to help patients and staff, and expressing appreciation for the interest of the staff and the facilities of the hospital.

The factor analysis of current behavior ratings uncovered the preceding ten factors, all of which are clinically significant and recognizable. However, there was little differentiation between the group containing 96 depressives and the small control groups, except in the category of apathy and indifference (Factor 3) and agitation (Factor 7) (Chapter 9).

Tests revealed that the check lists of current behavior achieved a respectable level of reliability. The check list of the stereotypes held by resident psychiatrists and graduate nurses disclosed four factors, of which only one was strong. The factors serve as a list of frequency of behavioral symptoms expected to be demonstrated by depressed patients, rather than disclosing types of syndromes. This fact further substantiates our reasoning concerning the absence of a "behavioristic" point of view utilized by psychiatric professionals, for even their stereotypes are listings of all possible behaviors that have been seen. Patients are not typed as to behavior, and correspondingly conceptual correlations are not entertained (Chapter 10).

Our research design did not include the goal of correlating personal data such as age, education, religion, etc., with symptoms and types of depression. Hence our available information concerning these items is scanty. Nevertheless, correlations were made and turned out to be statistically not significant or only weak. Those that are suggestive include the following: clinging depressives less frequently or only late receive electric shock treatment by psychoanalytically oriented psychiatrists; Catholics seem lower on feelings and concerns than others (perhaps less expressive); older patients have more aggravated or "bad" external signs of depression; males are higher in the "psychomotor rigidity" factor, and current behavior is correlated with personal data more than feelings and concerns, suggesting that the behavior in depression is more an expression of the patient's "life style" than of the basic pathology and should show a strong relationship or similarity with the patient's premorbid personality (Chapter 11).

Correlations between factors derived from *within* each check list revealed obvious relationships but nothing striking. On the other hand, correlations *between* the two sets of factors from the two trait lists were not present. Again we conclude that feelings are not expressed by specific behaviors but that behaviors are individually predetermined ways of responding and not closely related to the central or basic core process of the type of depression.

Factor *patterns* were developed from the combination of 15 factors of both trait lists. As a result, four factor patterns were elicited from which clinical profiles can be described to serve as fairly sharp hypotheses for future testing (Chapter 12). The factor patterns are as follows:

A. *Feelings*: Dismal, hopeless, loss of self-esteem, slight guilt feelings.

   Behavior: Isolated, withdrawn, apathetic, speech and thinking slowed with some cognitive disturbances.

B. *Feelings*: Hopeless with low self-esteem, considerable guilt feelings, high anxiety.

   Behavior: Agitation and clinging demands for attention.

C. *Feelings*: Abandonment and loss of love.

   Behavior: Agitated, demanding, hypochondriacal.

D. *Feelings*: Gloom, hopelessness, and anxiety.

   Behavior: Demanding, angry, provocative.

DISCUSSION

In each of the preceding chapters we have discussed the findings therein reported and summarized the specific conclusions presented. Now we shall make some more general statements.

In the first place, why were we especially interested in depressions? The statistics that we quoted in the introductory chapter indicate that this syndrome is encountered most frequently by psychiatrists in office and hospital practice. Nevertheless, active treatment has until recently been ineffective. Psychiatrists treated depressions with a variety of intuitive methods: some were supported and encouraged during weekly visits; others were handled with a directive, sometimes punitive manner. Some were placed in the then-popular "rest cures," while the seriously depressed were incarcerated in sanitariums away from their home cities to wait out a spontaneous recovery. In general, depressions were considered to be self-limited and therapy at best was only palliative alleviation of misery with reassuring words and sedation.

As time went on, the psychoanalytic theories encouraged psychiatrists to utilize psychoanalytic techniques either in the classical form or in modified psychotherapy, with many fine successes in the treatment and prevention of further attacks in neurotic or mild depressive patients. Yet with the advent of psychiatric units attached to general hospitals, the preponderance of admissions consisted of seriously depressed patients who were agitated, suicidal, withdrawn, or psychotic. For many of these psychotherapy offered little promise, and electric shock therapy and recently pharmacotherapy became the treatments of choice.

These patients were discussed at staff meetings and at teaching clinical conferences. Although psychodynamic formulations satisfied the curiosity of many regarding the specific psychogenics, these formulations were mostly stereotypes—one could always find evidences for what one wanted. But what we really needed was a more adequate explanation of the most frequent illness requiring our attention. Psychosomatic studies, despite the term "endogenous" were bogged down because there was no fruitful subdivision of the vast category of depressions.

We decided to conduct a clinical study of depression, hoping that an orderly representation of various components of the syndrome could further our knowledge and enable us to classify subgroups. But the amount of information we acquired from our pilot studies interfered with our scanning attempt and made it necessary to deal with our data statistically. Despite our qualms, the statistical methods were effective without sacrificing the "living" quality of our case material.

The pilot study utilized a detailed protocol for inquiry and observations, and careful interviews of patients were converted for the method of Q-sorts, and factor-analyzed. The results for feelings and concerns were three meaningful factors. Subsequently, using a check list derived from the pilot study, five factors were extracted for feelings and concerns in the full-scale research.

On the other hand, reliability of behavioral data from the pilot studies was not high enough for statistical analysis, a fact that haunted us throughout the research. Correspondingly, the stereotype of feelings and concerns of depressed patients was composed of a single sharply defined factor as contrasted with the vague stereotypes of behavior. The latter seems to be a collection of traits that have no obvious relationship to each other and are not recognizable as descriptive of people. The feelings and concerns stereotype did not bind the rater, for they went beyond its confines to find three factors in the pilot study and five in the full-scale research.

Corresponding to the above problems concerning rating of patients, behavior does not seem to be an accurate representation of what a person is thinking or feeling, at least in our sample. The behavioral manifestations of our patients which produced good, statistically sound factors do not correlate with affects or psychological content.

However, the development of a method of analysis which combined the feelings and behavior factors resulted in four significant and meaningful *factor patterns*.

Some traits which we might expect, a priori, to be important in depression do not appear in our factors. These include: loss of interest in oral satisfactions, ideas of committing suicide, fatigue, desire to cry much of the time, feeling of loss of esteem by others, relief after hospitalization, and ambivalence toward important personal issues. These items have a high standard deviation, which means that they vary from patient to patient, but they are not covariant with any of our factors. These must be regarded as "specifics" for depression as a total syndrome, not relating to any separate factor. Further study of some of these items might be useful.

Our experience during the pilot phase of the study, when careful psychiatric work-ups were completed and discussed in conference, indicated that rarely was there a depression with a single, clearcut precipitating event or experience. We found almost invariably a series of events that led up to the clincal illness. We also found that it was rare for the research group to reach a consensus on a formulation of the patients' psychodynamics.

Although we were not able to determine why a particular person became depressed (premorbid personality, precipitating factors, and psychodynamics), we were able to subdivide the syndrome into subcategories. Included in our interesting findings were the factors which seemed basic to depressions in general: Factor I (despair and hopelessness) and Factor IV (anxiety), which seemed to indicate activity, either regressive or progressive. The remaining factors probably indicate types of syndromes characterized by modes of defense against, and resolution of, the depressive affect.

In our discussion of the literature, Schmale's (1958) work was mentioned, for it embodied the hypothesis that real, anticipated, or fantasied object-loss preceded the onset of a wide variety of physical illnesses. Yet none of our depressed patients was plagued by more than transient symptoms, such as constipation, dry mouth, decreased sebum secretion, etc. Even the patients who were purest in Factor 9, the psychosomatic factor, showed no evidence of somatic disease. Schmale, of course, does not correlate depressions with somatic illness or its onset, but the hopeless and helpless affects and object-loss are identical with traits in our source list. Does the depressive affect substitute for or protect against physical illness, or are long-term follow-up studies necessary to establish the relationship? At any rate, we were unable to confirm Schmale's findings.

Much still remains to be done, and we hope others will also carry on further, using, if confirmed, the results of our research as a point of departure. We should like to improve on our ability to observe and record behavior. Comparative studies are needed with depressed state hospital patients, schizophrenics, and medically ill depressed patients. We need larger control groups similar to our O-D, D-O, and O-O groups. Further explorations into clinical agreements and disagreements are necessary, especially with refer- ence to the age, experience, orientation, and motivation of the observing personnel. We should attempt to translate categories of factors more concretely into clinical profiles that could enable us to identify the position of individual patients within the spectrum of depressions. Finally, correlations between our clinical subgroups and a variety of other clinical observations should be attempted.

CONCLUSIONS

Our research has developed a number of factors: five feelings and concerns, ten current behaviors, and, combining the two sets, four factor patterns. These are now available for correlations with demographic data; variations in premorbid personality; type of onset; precipitating factors; physical disease; course; amenability to psychotherapy, shock therapy, pharmacotherapy, milieu ther- apy, etc.; prognosis; relapses; and accurate physiological, endocrin- ological, biochemical, EEG, etc., measurements.

We hope that our investigations will stimulate efforts for im- provement in methodology. Among the serious problems are the difficulty experienced by psychiatrists in observing, recording, and conceptualizing behavior patterns in the mentally ill, the elusiveness of clear definitive premorbid personalities, precipitating factors, and unstereotyped psychodynamics. The pathetically inadequate routine hospital records, which can in no way be trusted for use in

References

ABRAHAM, K. (1953). "Notes on the Psycho-analytical Investigation and Treatment of Manic-Depressive Insanity and Allied Conditions" and "A Short Study of the Development of the Libido Viewed in the Light of Mental Disorders. Part I: Manic-Depressive States and the Pre-genital Levels of the Libido," in *Selected Papers of Karl Abraham*. New York, Basic Books.

ARIETI, S. (ed.) (1959). *American Handbook of Psychiatry*. New York, Basic Books, vol. 1, chap. 22.

Association for Research in Nervous and Mental Diseases (1931). Vol. II: *Manic Depressive Psychosis*, Baltimore, Williams and Wilkins.

BECK, S. J. (1954). The Six Schizophrenias. *Res. Monogr. Amer. Orthopsychiat. Ass.*, No. 6.

BECK, S. J. (1956). Concerning Researchers' Thinking in Schizophrenia. *Am. J. Orthopsychiat. 26*:792.

BELLAK, L. (1952). *Manic-Depressive Psychoses and Allied Conditions*. New York, Grune & Stratton.

BENEDEK, T. (1956). Toward the Biology of the Depressive Constellation. *J. Am. Psychoanalyt. A. 4*:389.

BIBRING, E. (1953). "The Mechanism of Depression," in *Affective Disorders*, ed. by Greenacre, P. New York, International Universities Press.

BLEULER, E. (1911). *Lehrbuch der Psychiatrie*, 9th ed., ed. Bleuler, M. (1955). Berlin, Springer.

BOARD, F., WADESON, R., and PERSKY, H. (1957). Depressive Aff and Endocrine Function. *Arch. Neurol. and Psychiat. 78*:612.

CASSIDY, W. L., FLANAGAN, M. D., SPELLMAN, M., and COHEN, M (1957). Clinical observations in manic-depressive disease. *J.A.M 164*:1535.

CLEGHORN, R. A., and CURTIS, G. C. (1959). Psychosomatic acc paniments of latent and manifest depressive affect. *Canad. Psyc A. J. 4*:513, Special Supplement.

COHEN, M. B., BAKER, G., COHEN, R. A., FROMM-REICHMANN, F. WEIGERT, E. (1954). An intensive study of twelve cases of r depressive psychosis. *Psychiatry 17*:103.

LANGE, J. (1928). *Handbuch der Geisteskrankheiten.* Berlin, Springer, vol. 2.

LEHMANN, H. E. (1959). Psychiatric concepts of depression: nomenclature and classification. *Canad. Psychiat. A. J. 4*:1. Special Supplement.

LEWIS, A. (1936). Manic-depressive psychosis; melancholia: prognostic study and case material. *J. Ment. Sc. 82*:488.

LEWIS, A. (1944). Depression. *J. Ment. Sc. 90*:256.

LICHTENBERG, P. (1957). A definition and analysis of depression. *Arch. Neurol. and Psychiat. 77*:519.

MENDELSON, M. (1960). *Psychoanalytic Concepts of Depression.* Springfield, Thomas.

MUNCIE, W. (1948). Psychobiology and Psychiatry, 2nd ed. St. Louis, Mosby.

OKEN, D., GRINKER, R. R., HEATH, H., SABSHIN, M., and SCHWARTZ, N. (1960). Stress response in a group of chronic psychiatric patients. *Arch. Gen. Psychiat. 3*:451.

RADO, S. (1928). The problem of melancholia. *Internat. J. Psycho-Analysis 9*:420.

ROSENFELD, H. (1959). An investigation into the psycho-analytic theory of depression. *Internat. J. Psycho-Analysis 40*:105.

ROTH, M. (1959). The phenomenology of depressive states. *Canad. Psychiat. A. J. 4*:532, Special Supplement.

ROTH, M. (1960). The phobic anxiety-depersonalization syndrome and some general etiological problems in psychiatry. *J. Neuropsychiat. 1*:293.

ROTH, M. (1960). Depressive states and their borderlands: classification, diagnosis and treatment. *Comprehensive Psychiatry 1*:135.

SCHMALE, A. H. (1958). Relation of separation and depression to disease. *Psychosom. Med. 20*:259.

SPITZ, R. (1945). "Hospitalism," in *The Psychoanalytic Study of the Child,* ed. by Freud, A., Hartmann, H., and Kris, E. New York, International Universities Press, vol. 1.

SPITZ, R. (1946). "Anaclitic Depression," in *The Psychoanalytic Study of the Child,* ed. by Freud, A., Hartmann, H., and Kris, E. New York, International Universities Press, vol. 2.

WEISS, E. (1944). Clinical aspects of depression. *Psychoanalyt. Quart. 13*:445.

WHITWELL, J. R. (1936). *Historical Notes on Psychiatry.* London, Lewis.

ZETZEL, E. (1953). "The Depressive Position," in *Affective Disorders,* ed. by Greenacre, P. New York, International Universities Press.

ZILBOORG, G. (1944). *A History of Medical Psychology.* New York, Norton.

Index